Wildflowers of the Sefton Coast

Philip H. Smith

Ploughman's Spikenard, *Inula conyzae*, Birkdale

GW00535879

Cover images:
  front: Grass-of-Parnassus, Cabin Hill NNR
  rear top: Mobile dunes, Ravenmeols LNR
  rear bottom: Hawkweeds, Cabin Hill NNR

Smith, P. H. 2021. *Wildfowers of the Sefton Coast*. Lancashire & Cheshire Fauna Society, Rishton
ISBN: 978-1-9169034-0-1

Printed by Ellison Printing, Rishton, Lancashire

CONTENTS

PREFACE

This book is about one of the richest areas for vascular or 'higher' plants (flowering plants, conifers and ferns) in Northwest England, namely the Sefton Coast, north of Liverpool. A low-lying 'soft' coast dominated by wind-blown dunes and extensive saltmarshes, it has enthused botanists, both amateur and professional, for well over 200 years. Thus, writing as a 'modern British traveller' in about 1805, George Alexander Cook states:

"To the lovers of botany, and natural curiosities, the sand hills and the shores will furnish an inexhaustible fund of amusement from the great quantities of flowers, plants and shells with which they abound."

The earliest published plant list for the area so far discovered is Peter Whittle's 1831 'Catalogue of plants found in the vicinity of Southport.' He writes evocatively:

"It is out of the question to take an excursion in the summer months, without being struck by the great number of elegant and pretty plants in full flower, many of which are found near the sea shore."

Whittle goes on to discuss many of the characteristic coastal flowers, including Sea Holly, Grass-of-Parnassus, Hound's-tongue and even the uncommon Yellow Bartsia. Nearly 200 years on, it is still possible to find most of his listed species.

In the book, I have described the typical wildflowers associated with each of the Sefton Coast's main habitats from the saltmarshes and 'green beaches' to the sand-dunes, the latter showing a sequence of successional stages running inland, from the newly-formed strandline and embryo dunes, through mobile and fixed-dunes to older woodland and dune-heath. Increasing interest in non-native or 'alien' plants is reflected in a chapter on these sometimes invasive but often innocuous and colourful additions to our flora. They already represent nearly 40% of the recorded higher plants and the number of aliens is increasing each year, mainly as garden-escapes. Hybrids, some of them very rare and of conservation interest, also merit their own chapter. Then follows a section on seven 'special' plants that are particularly associated with the Sefton Coast and are rare elsewhere. All have been the subject of detailed surveys into their changing status, with recommendations for their conservation. Summaries of these and other studies are a particular feature of the book. Full accounts have been published in the scientific journals: Conservation Evidence, British & Irish Botany, BSBI News, New Journal of Botany and Watsonia. Next, thirteen 'key sites' along the coast are reviewed, with the aim of guiding the plant enthusiast to the best places at the right times. Threats to botanical diversity of the coast's habitats are described in the following chapter. Livestock grazing on the saltmarshes may reduce the variety of plants but this has been offset by the recent growth of new, ungrazed marshland. The main issue for the sand-dunes is vegetation overgrowth, leading to loss of bare sand and increased stability, together with rampant scrub development which can out-compete the dune plants. Among the various management techniques used to maintain suitable conditions for our sand-dune flora are scrub control, reintroduction of livestock grazing, mowing and turf-stripping. As a last resort, it may be necessary to translocate rare plants to save them from extinction or even reintroduce species that have been lost to habitats that are now suitable for them. Finally, I show how monitoring and recording the status of our wildflowers is crucial to their effective conservation.

Common or vernacular names of plants are used in the text, the scientific names being provided in Appendix 1. Nomenclature follows Clive Stace's New Flora of the British Isles, 4th edition (2019). All the photos are mine, except where indicated.

THE AUTHOR

Dr Phil Smith was born at Crosby, Liverpool and lived from the ages of two to nine at Ainsdale where he developed an early interest in sand-dunes and kept pet Natterjack Toads. After graduating in Zoology from University College London, he attended that University's Conservation Diploma course, before studying for a Ph.D. in entomology and conducting post-doctoral research for the International Biological Programme at Grange-over-Sands, Cumbria. Returning to Merseyside in 1968 as a Lecturer in Applied Biology at Liverpool Polytechnic (now John Moores University), Phil made extensive use of the Sefton Coast for both teaching and research. From 1970 to 2010 he was a Trustee and Council member of the Lancashire Wildlife Trust. He currently serves on the Board and Task Groups of the Sefton Coast Partnership and the Altcar Conservation Advisory Group. Having devoted over fifty years to the study and conservation of the coast's flora and fauna, he has often taken part in and organised volunteer surveys, while also leading guided walks and giving talks to interpret the area's wildlife for the general public. Phil has written over 500 scientific papers, articles and reports on the Sefton Coast. For the last thirteen years, he has compiled monthly 'wildlife notes' for the Formby Civic Society. His books include The Sands of Time (1999) and The Sands of Time Revisited (2009), these being introductions to the history and natural history of the Sefton sand-dunes. Phil is also a keen wildlife photographer, concentrating mainly on insects and plants. In 2002, he was awarded an MBE for services to nature conservation.

ACKNOWLEDGEMENTS

Many friends have been involved in the floral surveys that are highlighted in this book. I would like to thank particularly Mike Wilcox, from whom I learned a great deal. My main survey partner was Patricia Lockwood, whose enthusiasm and energy were boundless. I am also grateful to the following contributors in published studies: Claire Boardman, Mary Dean, Steve Cross, Ben Deed, Sally Edmondson, Eric Greenwood, Richard Hall, Catherine Highfield, Natalie Hunt, Alice Kimpton, Pauline Michell, Joshua Styles and Jesse Tregale. John Twibell kindly provided details of the Crymlyn Warren Dune Wormwood.

My special thanks goes to Dave Bickerton for producing and publishing this book.

Field Forget-me-not, Range Lane, Formby

MAP OF THE KEY SITES

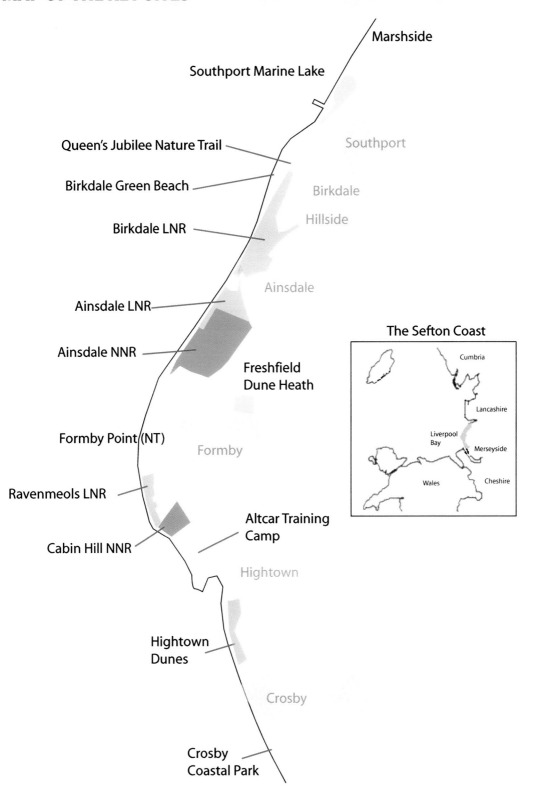

Marshside

Southport Marine Lake

Southport

Queen's Jubilee Nature Trail

Birkdale Green Beach

Birkdale

Hillside

Birkdale LNR

Ainsdale

Ainsdale LNR

Ainsdale NNR

Freshfield
Dune Heath

The Sefton Coast

Cumbria

Lancashire

Liverpool
Bay

Merseyside

Wales

Cheshire

Formby Point (NT)

Formby

Ravenmeols LNR

Altcar Training
Camp

Cabin Hill NNR

Hightown

Hightown
Dunes

Crosby

Crosby
Coastal Park

INTRODUCTION

Since the 1950s, native wildflowers have been lost from the British countryside at a rate of about one species per year per county. For the South Lancashire vice-county, which includes north Merseyside, the rate is roughly one species every two years and this loss is accelerating. Yet, on the outskirts of Liverpool, in one of the most urbanised parts of Britain, it is still possible to walk in high summer through a landscape vibrant with wildflowers. This inspirational place is the Sefton Coast, where rolling sand-dunes merge with the trackless saltmarshes of the Ribble Estuary.

Extending for about 25 km, the coastal zone includes the largest duneland in England (2100 ha). It is widely recognised as one of the most important examples of this habitat in Northwest Europe, supporting many iconic species of wildlife, such as the Natterjack Toad, Sand Lizard, Dune Helleborine and Northern Dune Tiger Beetle. Part of the great Ribble Estuary also lies within Sefton Borough.

Here, spectacular flocks of wading birds and waterfowl pass through on migration, about 250,000 staying for the winter. The coast attracts over a million human visitors every year, many coming to enjoy attractive landscapes and wildlife, with opportunities to walk for miles in stimulating surroundings. This area is also much used for teaching and research, having an international reputation amongst the scientific community.

I have long had a particular fascination for the flora of saltmarshes and sand-dunes. Many of the plants have evolved special adaptations to life in harsh maritime conditions and are rarely seen inland. Saltmarshes form in the relatively sheltered conditions of estuaries where fine silt particles, are deposited, building up mud-flats so they are exposed at low water. Plants are then able to colonise the mud surface. However, they have to cope with high salinity, lack of fresh-water, a water-logged soil lacking oxygen, mechanical scouring by the

Sand-dune panorama, Ravenmeols Local Nature Reserve, Formby

twice-daily tides and being covered in silt. It's not surprising that relatively few species have evolved these abilities, so saltmarshes support a small number of highly specialised plants.

Sand-dunes often form on the more exposed outer fringes of estuaries where there is more energy in the waves. As a result, only courser-grained materials fall out of suspension, creating a sandy foreshore. The open beach is so unstable and so exposed to wave-action that no higher plants can grow; they first appear on the strand-line where tidal litter makes it easier for a few hardy species to gain a foothold. However, they must be able to survive sand-blasting, salinity and occasional burial, as well as growing in a soil that is low in plant nutrients and moisture. When the beach dries out between high-tides, sand containing calcium-rich fragments of seashell is blown up the shore, being intercepted by strand-line plants to begin the process of dune formation. There follows a series of 'successional' stages - embryo, mobile and fixed-dunes, plants on the first two trapping increasing amounts of sand and growing up through the layers to continue this process. Each stage has its characteristic assortment of species, many of them requiring calcium in the soil. Walking inland from the beach, you are going back in time to dunes that were formed decades or even centuries in the past. The older 'fixed' dunes are more sheltered; most of the blowing sand has already been intercepted and there has been time for a thin soil to develop. Conditions are therefore easier for plant growth, allowing more species to survive. Even here, the soil is very low in essential nutrients and susceptible to summer drought. You would expect this to limit the flora but, in practice, the fixed-dunes are rich in flowering plants, partly because the poor nutrient supply prevents a few fast-growing competitive species taking over, dominating and crowding out the others.

Dune-slacks represent another important habitat. They are hollows between the dune ridges that flood with freshwater in winter, drying up during the summer. Their plants include specialists that prosper in the fluctu-ating wet/dry conditions. Older stages in dune development include grasslands, scrub and woodland. These add more species to the mix, though variety is lower than in the fixed-dunes and slacks. The final stage is dune-heath where the sand is several centuries old. There has been enough time for all the calcium to be washed out by rain, so that the soil is acidic enough to support Heather and other plants that like dry acid conditions.

The richness of the Sefton Coast's flora is one of its great attractions. This also contributes to a great variety of invertebrates, another of my main interests. Over 3300 of these 'minibeasts' have been recorded for the dune coast by World Museum Liverpool. One of my regular haunts is Freshfield Dune Heath Nature Reserve, owned and managed by the Lancashire Wildlife Trust. Despite its modest size (35 ha), the reserve supports an impressive total of 366 higher plants. Even more remarkable is its list of 1215 recorded inverte-brates, 1039 being insects. Many of these are heath and dune specialists, partly dependent on wildflowers. Coincidentally, the 2021 book on the *Bees, wasps and ants of Lancashire and North Merseyside* published by the Lancashire & Cheshire Fauna Society highlights the value of the Sefton dunes and dune-heath for these insects, citing the importance of sandy soils for nesting but also the rich plantlife that provides key resources, such as pollen and nectar.

Reflecting the importance of the Sefton Coast for nature, its habitats are protected by a raft of national and international conservation designations, including Site of Special Scien-tific Interest (SSSI), European Natura 2000 and RAMSAR. There are three National Nature Reserves (NNR), two Local Nature Reserves (LNR), an RSPB reserve, two County Wildlife Trust nature reserves and a large National Trust estate. In 2007, *Plantlife International* designated the Sefton dunes an 'Important Plant Area' (IPA), one of only 155 such sites in the UK.

COASTAL PLANTS AND THEIR HABITATS

The Sefton Coast has long been a magnet to botanists who come to see and study a bewildering variety of plants, including many hard to find elsewhere. In 1999, I started to compile an inventory of all the vascular plants (flowering plants, conifers and ferns) that had been recorded here. By late 2020, it included 1409 species, subspecies and hybrids for the coastal zone between Bootle and Marshside and 1249 on the sand-dunes. Remarkably, over 100 of them are grasses, representing 40% of the British grass flora. These totals include an increasing number of non-native species but not hundreds of 'lower' plants, such as mosses and algae, nor the fungi which are not classed as plants nowadays. The area is also a national 'hot-spot' for bryophytes (mosses and liver-worts) with around 230 species listed.

Rarities are well represented, around 230 of the higher plants being nationally or regionally 'notable'. About 75 species have become extinct here since the 19th century, 65 of them in the dunes. This might seem a lot but is a relatively small proportion overall. Also encouraging is the fact that 16 species thought lost were rediscovered between 1999 and 2007. Although plants have been recorded here since the early 19th century, we are still finding new ones, an average of 12 being added to the inventory each year since 2005.

This outstanding variety is a result of many factors, including the range of soils, from dry to wet, saline to non-saline and alkaline to acidic. Also important is the position of Sefton half-way up the west coast of Britain. This means there is a mix of plants with both northern and southern national distributions. For example, this is one of few places where both Northern and Southern Marsh-orchids can be found growing together.

Crucial to the success of the flora is the variety of habitats summarised in Table 1.

Table 1. Main habitats occupied by vascular plants in the inventory

Note: many species occur in more than one habitat

Habitat type	No. of occurrences	%
Disturbed ground	547	33
Slacks, scrapes, ponds & ditches	306	18
Fixed-dunes	235	14
Dune scrub	144	9
Dune grassland	137	8
Woodland	129	8
Saltmarsh	63	4
Dune-heath	63	4
Mobile & embryo dunes	28	1
Strandline & shingle	26	1

By far the largest number and proportion of plants (33%) are associated with disturbed ground. This includes patches of soil exposed naturally by wind-erosion or by Rabbit-burrowing but also land kept open by human activities, such as trampling, use of motor-vehicles, dereliction, tipping and agriculture. The next most important habitat is fresh-water wetland, represented by dune-slacks, scrapes, ponds and ditches (18%). Many of the duneland specialists depend on this habitat. Fixed-dune is also important (14%), both this and the dune-slack habitat being prior-ities for protection in Europe. Dune grassland and woodland (both 8%) are less valuable as habitats for plantlife on the coast, although they do have their specialities. The saline soils of the saltmarsh (4%) and the acidic dune-heath (4%) support fewer species because the conditions make it harder for plants to thrive. However, the lowest numbers of plants are found on embryo-dunes and the strandline (both 1%). This is because only a few species have evolved the ability to grow in such a hostile habitat with blowing sand, salt-spray, drought and lack of nutrients.

All plants live in associations or communities. These can be recognised and recorded using the UK's National Vegetation Classification (NVC). Most of the dune system was NVC surveyed in 1988/89 and again in 2003/04. Between the two surveys the area of some of the richest dune and dune slack communities declined, while non-dune neutral grassland increased. The reasons for these trends, which took place in only 15 years, are not fully understood. However, one important factor seems to be the build-up of nutrients in the soil due to scrub invasion, lack of grazing and the rain of pollutants (mostly nitrogen) from the air. These changes have been linked with declines of wildflowers nationally, especially in habitats that are otherwise low in nutrients, such as heathlands, lime-rich grasslands, peat-bogs and sand-dunes. Higher than normal nutrient levels encourage tall-growing plants, such as nettles, brambles and coarse grasses which can out-compete and replace the much greater variety of smaller plants.

The Sefton Coast provides a wide range of habitats for wildflowers, as at the 'Devil's Hole'

MAIN HABITATS AND THEIR CHARACTERISTIC WILDFLOWERS

Saltmarsh

A broad sweep of saltmarshes extends across the mouth of the Ribble Estuary, east of Southport. Due to the rapid build-up of silt and sand, these marshes have greatly expanded in recent decades, giving more protection against rising sea-levels for a low-lying coast. We are lucky, because in many other parts of the country saltmarsh is being lost to erosion. The plantlife can be divided into three overlapping zones, depending on the age of vegetation and degree of submergence by the twice-daily tides. Pioneer communities low down on the shore have several kinds of annual glass-worts, often in a sparse sward of Common Saltmarsh-grass with scattered patches of Common Cord-grass. Salt-resistant glassworts can be tricky to identify but the commonest species here is the distinctive Purple Glasswort which gives a reddish tinge to the marsh in autumn. The bright green Common Glasswort, greyish green Long-stalked Glasswort and, living up to its name, the 'nationally scarce' Yellow Glasswort can also be found. Above this zone, Common Saltmarsh-grass is dominant in the middle-marsh but there is an increasing variety of other plants, including Sea Aster whose lilac flowers colour the marsh in late summer, attracting bees and butterflies. A common white-flowered crucifer at Marshside in April/May was always thought to be English Scurvy-grass. However, research by Tim Rich and others suggests this is the similar Atlantic Scurvy-grass, or a mixture of the two.

In 2008, Patricia Lockwood and I searched the saltings off Hesketh Road, Marshside, discovering for the first time several plants of Common Sea-lavender and the 'nationally scarce' Lax-flowered Sea-lavender, the latter being new to the South Lancashire vice-county. More of both were found over the next few years, together with a few of the rare hybrid between them. By 2019, hundreds of sea-lavender plants were present, including a high proportion of young individuals from successful breeding.

Pioneer saltmarsh vegetation with glassworts at Marshside

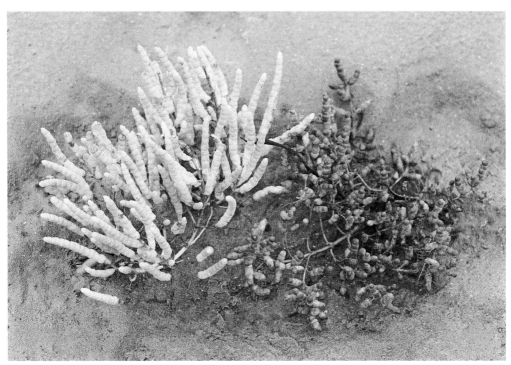

Long-stalked (left) and Purple Glasswort, Hightown shore

Maturing saltmarsh with Common Sea-lavender, Marshside, Southport

The rare Hybrid Sea-lavender at Marshside

The upper marsh supports many of the species already mentioned but also has swards of Red Fescue, often showing first on the tops of hummocks originally formed by silt deposited around Common Saltmarsh-grass. Well-drained creek edges have clumps of the woody Sea Purslane, while enriched soils of drift-lines close to the embankments support dense stands of Common Couch, Spear-leaved Orache and the big yellow blooms of Perennial Sowthistle. Checking the drift-lines at Marshside from 2015 onwards was rewarded by the discovery of the uncommon hybrids: Kattegat Orache and Taschereau's Orache, together with a few of the even rarer Long-stalked Orache.

Land at Marshside reclaimed from the estuary in the early 1970s and often flooded in winter is now part of the RSPB's Marshside Nature Reserve. Grazing by cattle has promoted a richly diverse plantlife typical of remnant saltmarsh, damp grassland and freshwater wetland. Colourful marsh-orchids,

mainly the Early Marsh-orchid and Southern Marsh-orchid, are often numerous. Large patches of yellow-flowered Buttonweed, a non-native introduction from South Africa or New Zealand, have recently been joined by the rare and spectacular Golden Dock. Many of these plants are easily visible from the bird hides.

Further south, along the dune coast, saltmarsh is mostly found in two areas, the mouth of the River Alt at Hightown and Birkdale Green Beach. The small saltmarsh at Hightown dates back to at least the 1930s. It has similar communities to Marshside, including the glassworts, but also a large bed of Common Reed where freshwater seepage enters the marsh from the dunes. At the back of the reed-marsh Common Meadow-rue can be found, together with a large colony of an uncommon coastal form (subspecies *roseata*) of the Hedge Bindweed, with beautiful pink-and-white striped, rather than white, flowers.

Golden Dock at Marshside RSPB reserve

Subspecies *roseata* of Hedge Bindweed, Hightown

Green Beach

Representing a transition between saltmarshes and sand-dunes, Birkdale Green Beach is a fascinating mix of saltmarsh, dune, dune-slack, swamp and wet-woodland. Its name derives from the Dutch 'groene stranden', referring to similar features in the Delta region of The Netherlands. The Green Beach began to develop in 1986 as patches of Common Saltmarsh-grass on the foreshore between Ainsdale and Birkdale. These trapped silt and sand, raising the beach level and allowing a greater range of species to move in. At present, the Green Beach is about 4 km long, up to 200 m wide and covers an area of over 65 ha. The northern section consists mainly of high-level saltmarsh, its plantlife including large patches of Hard-grass accompanying the usual Common Saltmarsh-grass and Red Fescue. Muddy areas support glassworts, two kinds of sea-spurrey and the regionally rare Frog Rush. There is also a spectacular abundance of pink-flowered Sea Milkwort, while Thrift and Saltmarsh Flat-sedge have appeared more recently. The latter is of particular interest, being one of few 'northern' plants of the saltmarsh community. It was presumed extinct in the vice-county until it was re-discovered during a BSBI field meeting in 2006. I conducted a careful search in 2012, finding 29 patches of Saltmarsh Flat-sedge scattered along the northern half of the Green Beach, growing with drifts of Sea Club-rush and Sea Rush.

The southern half of the Green Beach consists of an outer dune ridge with developing slacks behind. In 1998, Alder bushes began to appear in parallel lines in the older slacks, their origin being from seeds washing up on a sequence of flood- or strand-lines. Between the Alders, tall-fen vegetation developed, dominated by Common Reed but including patches of Bulrush, Sea Club-rush and Grey Club-rush.

The northern section of Birkdale Green Beach looking towards Black Combe in Cumbria

Green Beach central section showing lines of Alder bushes

Sea Milkwort, Birkdale Green Beach

Where the saline influence is reduced by fresh-water run-off from the dunes, brackish-water species include Long-bracted Sedge, Parsley Water-dropwort, Brookweed, Wild Celery and Lesser Water-parsnip. All are frequent on the Green Beach but hard to find elsewhere along the coast. Also part of this community is Slender Spike-rush, an often overlooked, declining wetland plant with a mainly northern British distribution. It was thought to be rare or absent from the Sefton Coast until I found a large colony at Crosby Coastal Park's boating lake in 2010. This prompted a wider survey, during which I recorded 45 patches of the plant, 34 of them being in upper saltmarsh or brackish swamp vegetation on Birkdale Green Beach. Overall, more than 350 higher plants have been identified on the Green Beach and new pioneer habitat is still forming to the south near Ainsdale-on-Sea, with opportunities to add to the species total.

Shingle

The only 'shingle' beach in Sefton is between Hightown and Hall Road where erosion of a tipped embankment has produced a zone of water-worn house bricks and other rubble. Despite its artificial origin, it supports a typical community of plants adapted to the harsh shingle environment. They have to be tough to withstand the movement of stones during storms and to tolerate saline conditions. Most attractive is the Yellow Horned-poppy with its large, bright-yellow flowers in June, grey foliage and strikingly long seed-pods. Also characteristic is Sea-kale, which large fleshy blue-green leaves and masses of white flowers. More often found on sea-cliffs, Rock Samphire has become well established in recent years. Yellow cushions of Biting Stonecrop often occupy gaps between the bricks. Vegetated shingle is a rare habitat in north-west England, being recognised as having conservation importance both in Britain and Europe. The shingle habitat was severely damaged by storm surges during the 2013/14 winter, few of its typical plants surviving. Fortunately, except for Sea-kale, most species recovered over the next few years, presumably from buried seed.

Hightown brick-rubble 'shingle' with Yellow Horned-poppy

Sea-kale on the 'shingle' beach at Blundellsands

Biting Stonecrop, Hightown shingle beach

Strandline

Strandline communities are sporadic on the Sefton Coast, well developed in some areas in some years and virtually absent at other times. They consist of a small number of hardy, mostly annual, plants that colonise the drift-line at the top of the beach and whose seeds are transported by the tide. Typical species, flowering in late summer, include the mauve-flowered Sea Rocket and the very spiny Prickly Saltwort, the latter being most frequent at Ravenmeols and Hightown. Often, Spear-leaved Orache is the commonest strandline species, sometimes accompanied by Sea Beet, while the related Frosted Orache, Grass-leaved Orache and Babington's Orache are a little harder to find. Also worth looking out for is the regionally rare Ray's Knotgrass with distinctive bluish-green leaves.

Birkdale Green Beach strandline with Sea Rocket

Prickly Saltwort on the strandline at Ravenmeols

Ray's Knotgrass on Birkdale Green Beach

Embryo dunes

The tough perennial grasses, Sand Couch and Lyme-grass, are uniquely adapted to harsh maritime conditions and generally dominate the embryo dunes. A few strandline plants may also make an appearance, particularly the ubiquitous Sea Rocket and Prickly Saltwort, while Sea Sandwort is found mainly at Hightown.

Embryo dunes with Lyme-grass, Birkdale Green Beach

Mobile-dunes

The capacity of the tall spiky Marram to trap sand, survive burial and grow up through thick layers of blown-sand makes this the dominant plant of the mobile-dunes and the main dune-forming species. It is also highly drought-resistant, its leaves having a thick, waxy cuticle and the ability to roll up into a tube to reduce water-loss. The importance of Marram to coastal dune development has been recognised for centuries. For example, Peter Whittle wrote in 1831:

"The sand hills, blown together in most irregular shapes, are held in these positions by the matted roots of the arundo arenaria – star, sea reed, marrum, or sea matweed. This is a useful and common plant on many of our sandy seashores. Its cultivation has, at various times been much encouraged, and even acts of parliament have been passed for its preservation, in consequence of its spreading roots giving stability to the loose, blowing sand, and thus raising a bulwark against the encroachment of the waves."

Marram dunes, Ainsdale Sandhills Local Nature Reserve

In gaps between the Marram tussocks and where sand-deposition is lower, a few other plants can gain a foothold, particularly quick-growing 'weedy' species such as Groundsel, Common Ragwort and Creeping Thistle. There is a rare coastal form of Groundsel, with short ligules on its ray-florets, found especially at the southern end of Birkdale Green Beach and at Crosby Coastal Park. Other typical plants of this community are the succulent Sea Spurge and Sea Holly, the latter's blue flowers being extremely attractive to duneland butter-flies, such as the Grayling (*Hipparchia semele*). Sprawling plants of yellow-flowered Sea Radish can also be found in this habitat. A rare but characteristic plant of the mobile dunes is the beautiful Sea Bindweed. When I surveyed it with Patricia Lockwood in 2010, only six patches were found between Hightown and Marshside. Being rather shy of flowering, it is mainly recognised by its kidney-shaped fleshy leaves.

On the older mobile dunes, especially the back-slopes, there is often a broad zone of vegetation intermediate between mobile and fixed-dunes. Marram is still abundant here but the reduced rain of blown-sand allows a much greater range of species to move in. Among the grasses, Red Fescue and Spreading Meadow-grass can often be common, while tall herbs, such as Rosebay Willowherb and Umbellate Hawkweed, lend a splash of colour, sometimes accom-panied by the striking flowers of Ploughman's Spikenard, named from its earlier reputation as a curative herb, especially for wounds. Ground-hugging species, also with attractive flowers, include Common Restharrow, Heath Dog-violet and, less often, the richly coloured Dune Pansy. Potentially confusing yellow-flowered dandelion look-alikes also put in an appearance, the commonest being Cat's-ear and the more delicate Smooth Hawk's-

Maritime form of Groundsel, Crosby Coastal Park

Sea Bindweed, Hightown dunes

Sea Holly at Crosby dunes

Dune Pansy, Ainsdale Sandhills Local Nature Reserve

Common Restharrow, Birkdale dunes

Fixed-dunes

beard. The non-native Beaked Hawk's-beard is increasing and may also be encountered.

This is the most extensive dune habitat on the Sefton Coast and designated for special protection throughout Europe. Here, the dunes are older and there has been enough time for some organic matter to be incorporated into the thin soil making conditions suitable for a wider variety of plants. Although the ground surface is mostly well vegetated, there are still bare sandy patches, providing a seed-bed for many species, especially annuals. Sefton Coast sand has about 5% calcium carbonate derived from seashells. It is well known that more plants can grow in calcareous soils than in acid ones, so the younger fixed-dunes are favoured by many lime-loving species. Typical examples are Common Centaury, Yellow-wort, Carline Thistle, Lady's Bedstraw and the lovely Blue Fleabane. This group also includes members of the pea family, such as Common Bird's-foot-trefoil, Hare's-foot Clover and Kidney Vetch,

the latter producing golden drifts of flowers in mid-summer, attracting great numbers of bumblebees.

Blue Fleabane, Birkdale sand-dunes

Kidney Vetch on fixed-dunes, Birkdale Green Beach

Common Bird's-foot-trefoil, Birkdale Green Beach fixed-dunes

Several orchids also favour limy soils. The bright-pink Pyramidal Orchid is now much more abundant than it was 30 years ago. There are large colonies at Cabin Hill NNR and Ainsdale Sandhills LNR, both containing thousands of flower-spikes, amongst which a rare white form can occasionally be found. The spectacular Bee Orchid is also easy to see in most years and, like the Pyramidal Orchid, seems to be increasing, perhaps due to climate change. A scarcer lime-lover is Viper's-bugloss, whose dramatic purple-blue spikes are especially prevalent on the Hightown dunes. The low-growing, white Burnet Rose is also a Hightown speciality.

The rarest of Sefton's fixed-dune plants is probably Dyer's Greenweed, a small deciduous shrub of the pea family with golden flowers that is Red-listed 'vulnerable' in England. There are two small patches near the coast road on Birkdale LNR. It was still there in 2017 but is clearly susceptible to scrub development or inadvertent damage from road works. Sadly, one species that didn't survive the overgrowth of coarse vegetation is the strange-looking miniature fern, Moonwort. I didn't realise it at the time but, on 3rd July 1983, I photographed the last plant on Ainsdale NNR and it hasn't been seen here since.

Pyramidal Orchid, Ainsdale LNR, normal (left) and white form (right)

Bee Orchid, Devil's Hole

Viper's-bugloss, Hightown dunes

Dyer's Greenweed, Birkdale dunes

One of the most familiar fixed-dune plants is Dewberry, a sand-dune bramble that E.D. McNicholl (1883) knew well:

"In late summer they are loaded with the handsome fruit, at once distinguished from blackberries by the great size and the fewness of the component drupeolae, which are covered, moreover, with a delicate glaucous bloom instead of being jetty and shining."

Dewberry in fruit, Larkhill, Formby

An interesting feature of the fixed-dunes is the effect of slope and aspect. Cooler and damper north-facing slopes have a more luxuriant sward characterised by the Common Polypody fern and Wood Sage, together with Wild Strawberry and Sweet Vernal-grass. Drier south-facing slopes have sparser vegetation, often dominated by mosses and lichens and tiny spring-flowering annuals. Where the dune surface is damaged, for example by Rabbit-burrowing, trampling or wind-erosion, colonisers of bare ground are found. Examples include Bugloss, Common Stork's-bill, the 'nationally scarce' and paler-flowered Sticky Stork's-bill and the hybrid between the two, which can be recognised by its intermediate flowers, vigour and lack of seed pods. Although frequent on the Sefton Coast, this stork's-bill hybrid is a national rarity, being confined to dunes in Wales, north Wirral and South Lancashire. Portland Spurge and Hound's-tongue are other members of this plant community. The latter is listed as 'near threatened' in the Red Data Book, though it is common on the Sefton Coast.

Sticky Stork's-bill, Range Lane, Formby

Hybrid Stork's-bill, Ravenmeols dunes

Some of the most fascinating flowers of the bare patches are the dune (or winter) annuals. These miniature plants from several unrelated families (Table 2) have evolved the same strategy for overcoming the problem of summer drought. Their seeds germinate during the autumn rains and the small plants survive the winter, ready to grow and flower as temperatures rise in the spring. By the time the soil begins to dry out in May, they have shed their drought-tolerant seeds and then die down completely. Although tiny, most are visually attractive, a favourite being the Early Forget-me-not with its brilliant blue flowers.

Hound's-tongue, Formby Point

It was a complete surprise when Patricia Lockwood and I found Rough Clover, a new member of this group of annuals, during a guided wildflower walk at Ainsdale in June 2012. This little white-flowered clover had never been seen before in the vice-county. Even rarer is the Early Sand-grass, confined to a handful of British sites. It flowers in great abundance during March and early April on the dunes west of Southport Marine Lake (see 'special plants'). Disturbed ground also favours the dandelion, that most familiar of wildflowers. It is not always appreciated that there are about 250 species of dandelion in Britain, 30 being listed for the Sefton Coast. During a 2020 survey, Joshua Styles added another eleven to the dune inventory, three of them rated 'nationally scarce'.

Two dune annuals: Early Forget-me-not (left) and Rough Clover (right)

Early Sand-grass, Southport Marine Lake dunes

Table 2. Common dune annuals on the Sefton Coast dunes.

English name	Scientific name	Plant family
Hairy Bitter-cress	*Cardamine hirsuta*	Cabbage
Common Whitlowgrass	*Erophila verna*	Cabbage
Thyme-leaved Sandwort	*Arenaria serpyllifolia*	Pink
Sea Mouse-ear	*Cerastium diffusum*	Pink
Little Mouse-ear	*Cerastium semidecandrum*	Pink
Rue-leaved Saxifrage	*Saxifraga tridactylites*	Saxifrage
Early Forget-me-not	*Myosotis ramosissima*	Borage
Common Cornsalad	*Valerianella locusta*	Valerian
Spring Vetch	*Vicia lathyroides*	Pea
Early Hair-grass	*Aira praecox*	Grass
Sand Cat's-tail	*Phleum arenarium*	Grass
Dune Fescue	*Vulpia fasciculata*	Grass

Some areas of fixed-dune are several centuries old. Over time, most of the calcium has been washed out by rainfall, making the sandy soil more acidic. Colourful constituents of these older dunes are the delicate Harebell and fragrant Wild Thyme. Another beauty that can be found on both acid and alkaline soils is Common Milkwort. It comes in a wide range of colours, from pink to white or blue.

Southport & Ainsdale Golf Course has some of the oldest dunes and here the Grey Hair-grass occurs in the 'roughs'. One of our most beautiful grasses, this national rarity is mainly found in East Anglia. As it was first seen on the Sefton Coast in 1919, it seems unlikely to have been introduced and is accepted as native here. My survey of the golf course with Patricia Lockwood in 2007 showed that Grey Hair-grass had increased over the previous decade. With an estimated 10,000 plants, this may be the largest colony in Britain outside North Norfolk and the Channel Isles.

Harebells, Birkdale frontal dunes

Blue form of Common Milkwort, Hightown dunes

Grey Hair-grass, Southport & Ainsdale Golf Course

Also found mostly on the more acid sands, the Smooth Cat's-ear is a diminutive, easily overlooked, member of the dandelion family. Its tiny yellow flowers open only in full sun during the morning and early afternoon. Although it was first recorded here in 1866, there had only been two sightings on the dunes in 50 years, until 2007 when the plant turned up in great numbers. I counted 5200 individuals in 28 duneland localities. However, it is still declining nationally because of agricultural 'improvement' and loss of grazing, especially by Rabbits and is therefore Red-listed as 'vulnerable'.

Smooth Cat's-ear, Ainsdale NNR

Dune grasslands

Tall grasslands occur extensively on the Sefton dunes, having noticeably increased in recent decades around slacks, scrub patches and on former agricultural land, as well as in some areas of fixed-dune. The coarse and unwelcome False Oat-grass often dominates, indicating absence of grazing and elevated soil nutrients. The beautiful Quaking-grass and Yellow Oat-grass appear occasionally, while stands of Downy Oat-grass are a feature of Birkdale Sandhills, Royal Birkdale Golf Course and Hightown dunes. A scarcer grass, Wood Small-reed, was found by Peter Gateley in 1997 on West Lancashire Golf Course and at Birkdale. There is also a sizeable patch of this striking plant west of Sands Lake, Ainsdale. However, it is very invasive on the Dutch dunes and is certainly spreading at Ainsdale, so vigilance is needed. Large herbs, such as hawkweeds, are a feature of these grasslands. There are also tall members of the carrot-family (umbellifers), such as Wild Parsnip and Wild Carrot, these being the original parents of the garden vegetables.

Dune grassland with hawkweeds, Ravenmeols Local Nature Reserve

Quaking-grass, Falklands Way, Ainsdale

Wood Small-reed near Sands Lake, Ainsdale

Our most interesting area of damp grassland is on the ranges of Altcar Training Camp where the authorities agreed to delay mowing in selected areas until mid-July, so that orchids and Cowslips could flower and set seed. This habitat now supports the largest population of Green-winged Orchids in the north of England. From the first discovery in 1984, Steve Cross's annual counts show a remarkable increase, peaking at over 30,000 flower-spikes. Steve and I showed that numbers hardly increased at all on an adjacent area where the mowing regime was not changed. Also present on the late-mowed ranges are many Southern, Early and Northern Marsh-orchids, together with hybrids, some of which have still to be identified. Adding to this colourful vista are pink stands of Ragged Robin, providing one of the great botanical spectacles on the coast.

Altcar Training Camp: damp grassland with Ragged Robin

35

Two unusual colour forms of Green-winged Orchid, Altcar Training Camp

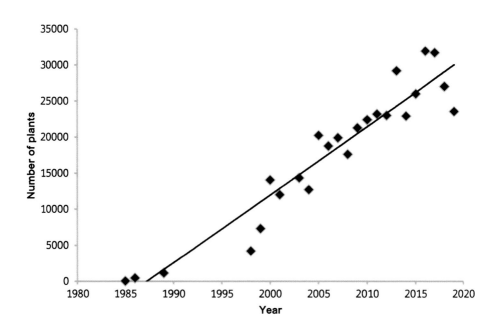

Counts of Green-winged Orchids at Altcar Training Camp, 1985-2019

On the eastern fringe of the dune system are a few areas of dry grassland on acidic soils, one of the largest being the 10 ha Birkdale

Annual Knawel, Birkdale Common

Common. A speciality here is Annual Knawel. Rapidly declining throughout the country, this plant is listed as 'endangered' in both the GB and England Red Data Books. It had been extinct in the dunes since 1914 before I rediscovered it in 2010. Unexpectedly, Joshua Styles found that the Annual Knawel population increased to several thousand individuals after the summer drought of 2018, which may have reduced its competitors. The following year, he showed me a few plants at Freshfield Dune Heath, a really notable addition to the reserve's list.

Also associated with acid grassland is the white-flowered Shepherd's-cress. This has seriously declined throughout its British range and is Red-listed as 'near threatened'. It has gone from many of its Sefton Coast localities and, by 2011, Patricia Lockwood and I could find it only on a small area of Rabbit-grazed grassland at Pinfold Meadow, Ainsdale NNR, where we estimated several hundred individuals. However, in 2013, Dave Earl found a new, much larger colony along the eastern edge of Woodvale Airfield. By 2015, this population had increased spectacularly to uncountable thousands. This seemed to be linked to the occasional use of herbicide to kill off competitive vegetation along a fence line. The timing of this treatment was evidently crucial to the survival of this spring-flowering annual.

Exceptional population of Shepherd's-cress, Woodvale airfield boundary fence

Road verges

Especially at Ainsdale and Hightown, grassy roadside verges have been created from sand-dunes within living memory. The verges are 'managed' by occasional mowing. Impoverished soils and summer drought prevent taller-growing more competitive species taking over. As a result, I was fascinated to find that several of the verges had developed a flora similar to Rabbit-grazed dune grassland. Those at Kenilworth Road, Ainsdale and Thornbeck Avenue, Hightown are especially rich, with around 80 different plants recorded on each, including the uncommon Knotted Clover, Slender Trefoil and Clustered Clover. The latter is mainly found in southern England, being unknown elsewhere in the Northwest. Depending on the frequency of mowing and drought, these verges can be extremely attractive in early summer, with colourful patches of flowering clovers, Common Bird's-foot-trefoil and Dove's-foot Crane's-bill. The 'nationally rare' Smooth Rupturewort occurs in some abundance on the Kenilworth Road verges, being also found sparingly on the nearby Westminster Drive, at Westcliffe Road, Southport, and Crosby Coastal Park. A low-growing habit helps it to survive mowing. As a native species, this plant is largely confined to eastern England, its origin in Sefton probably being as a garden-escape.

Clustered Clover, Thornbeck
Avenue verges, Hightown

Smooth Rupturewort Kenilworth
Road verge, Ainsdale

Dune-scrub

Dune-scrub is a natural stage in sand-dune succession, occurring mainly in older parts of the fixed-dunes where increasing shelter and improving soil conditions allow woody plants to become established. On the Sefton Coast, scrub is surprisingly rich in species, the inventory listing 144 vascular plants primarily associated with this habitat (9% of the flora). The downside is that many of these shrubby species are non-native, including lots of garden-escapes. Since the 1950s, dune-scrub has increased enormously in extent, invading areas of fixed-dune and dune grassland. This is due to a combination of factors, including the reduction in Rabbit and livestock-grazing and the fertilising action of nitrogen deposited from the air.

Willows are a major component of dune-scrub in damper areas. Our dunes are one of the richest parts of the country for these shrubs. Mike Wilcox and I have recorded over 30 different kinds, fifteen being hybrids and several nationally rare (see section on 'hybrids'). However, their origin was not always natural; several were planted in the past for basket-making.

Freshwater seepage along the inner edge of Birkdale Green Beach has encouraged the development of Alder scrub since the late 1990s. Despite the stunting effects of salty winds, the trees, currently up to 23 years old, are more than 3 m tall. They form an important 'wet woodland' habitat rich in invertebrates. Alder woodland so close to the sea is unusual, as this wetland tree is not known to have any tolerance of salt-water. There are even older stands of Alder in former dune-slacks, especially on Ainsdale NNR.

Dune scrub on fixed-dunes, Birkdale Sandhills Local Nature Reserve

Alder on Birkdale Green Beach

Woodland

Most of the woodland on the dune coast is made up of conifers planted by the former manorial estates from the 1880s to about the 1930s, though there have also been some more recent plantings, especially on Altcar Training Camp. Conifer plantations now occupy about 260 ha, most of the trees being Corsican Pine from the Mediterranean, a tree that is well adapted to seaside conditions. Also commonly planted was Scots Pine, while other conifers, such as Lodgepole and Maritime Pine are much rarer. Broad-leaved woodland is less extensive but has increased greatly in recent decades as scrub patches have matured. A variety of species includes the native Silver Birch and Downy Birch but also introduced poplars, such as Balm-of-Gilead, Grey Poplar and White Poplar. Sycamore is also frequent. The most interesting of the planted trees is Black Poplar. This is a rare native, typically found on river flood-plains in the Midlands and Southern England. National surveys in the 1990s found only about 7000 of them. The Sefton trees, all male, were mostly planted in the late 19th and early 20th centuries to provide shelter on the fringes of pine plantations on asparagus field boundaries and along the edges of tracks. My 2008/09 study with Patricia Lockwood mapped 650 of them on Formby Point, some estimated to be over 120 years old. These venerable trees are characterised by leaning trunks, down-sweeping branches and up-sweeping amber twigs. Larger limbs often layer into the ground, sending up new stems that may eventually mature into substantial trees. Their distinctive red catkins make a fine show in late March.

Layering Black Poplar, Ravenmeols

Black Poplar catkins, Ravenmeols

Green-flowered Helleborine in conifer plantation,
Ainsdale

Because of dense shade, the ground flora of conifer woodland is often limited to a few species of ferns. Notable exceptions, however, are the nationally important Dune Helleborine and Green-flowered Helleborine, a 2008/09 coastwide volunteer study led by Pauline Michell revealing that about 70% of both species grew in pine plantations (see section on 'special plants').

Common Wintergreen grows in acid soils on the fringes of birch or pine woodland at Formby Point and Ainsdale NNR. In 2017, Patricia Lockwood and I counted nearly 11,400 plants in 18 colonies. Excluding Cumbria, this is the only sizeable population in Northwest England of a species that is Red-listed as 'near threatened' in England. Also rather local in shady places on the dunes is Lords-and-Ladies, also known as Cuckoo-pint. The strange purple cowl or spadix heats up and emits an odour that attracts small midges for pollination. The rather similar non-native Italian Lords-and-Ladies has a yellow cowl and strongly patterned leaves.

Common Wintergreen, Ainsdale NNR

Lords-and-Ladies, Ravenmeols

Dune-heath

Areas of dune-heath are found on the eastern edge of the dune system. It takes about 300 years for rainfall, which is slightly acidic, to remove all the calcium from the sand, creating conditions suitable for the development of heathland. Much of the surviving dune-heath is found on former agricultural land or on golf courses, consisting of old fixed-dunes or level areas of 'links' sand blown off the dunes in past centuries. This is a rare habitat nationally and a priority for conservation. Heather and 'weed' pollen were detected in drilled core samples near Crosby dated to 2700 years ago, showing that early settlers were removing trees, growing crops and producing soil conditions that allowed heathland to develop. However, a study of floras and other published works from the 19th and early 20th centuries found no reference to Heather on the dune backlands before 1923. This is presumably because these areas were used intensively for livestock rearing and arable cropping, which replaced Heather by grazing-tolerant grasses. Once it became uneconomic to farm these acid soils, Heather began to appear.

Peter Gateley's 1993/94 survey mapped 154 ha of what he broadly defined as dune-heath, compared with only about 200 ha in total on all English dune systems. The largest block is now within the Lancashire Wildlife Trust's Freshfield Dune Heath Nature Reserve established in 2004 on the southern boundary of Woodvale Aerodrome. Another representative example is Larkhill Heath at Formby on the National Trust estate. Both contain large stands of Heather, which puts on a wonderful show in late summer and also much Gorse, seen at its best in spring. Montagu Road Triangle, north of Freshfield station, was wall-to-wall heathland 40 years ago but invasion by birch and pine had shaded out much of the Heather, until Natural England organised major works to restore the habitat in 2020/21.

Freshfield Dune Heath Nature Reserve; Heather flowering in late summer

Freshfield Dune Heath Nature Reserve in spring with flowering Gorse

The most frequent plants associated with the Heather are Common Bent, Cat's-ear, Field Wood-rush, Sand Sedge, Sheep's-fescue, Sheep's Sorrel and Wavy Hair-grass. With a little more effort, the acid-tolerant Heath-grass and Mat-grass can be found, while damper hollows support the equally characteristic Heath Rush. Two uncommon plants on the dune-heath are the diminutive Bird's-foot, and the yellow-flowered Trailing St John's-wort. Also rare in the Northwest is Fine-leaved Sheep's-fescue, which is a real challenge to identify. A patch of the usually upland Crowberry was found at Woodvale during Peter Gateley's survey. Later, he discovered two more colonies on Formby Ladies Golf Course. Larkhill Heath has the coast's only bush of Eared Willow, a shrub typical of acid heaths and moorlands.

Sheep's Sorrel, Freshfield Dune Heath

Bird's-foot, Freshfield Dune Heath

Trailing St John's-wort, Larkhill Heath, Formby

Dune-slacks

In the valleys between dune ridges or where sand has been blown down to the natural water-table, seasonally flooded dune-slacks are found. Similar wetlands have been created by human activities, such as past sand-winning or the excavation of scrapes and ponds for conservation purposes. Depending on the amount of rainfall, especially that which falls in winter, the slacks can be deeply flooded from autumn to early summer but in drought years they may hold little or no surface water. Most tend to dry out by mid-summer. The Sefton Coast is particularly well-endowed with slacks, about 350 having been mapped, representing over a third of the English extent of this habitat. Dune-slacks are a threatened habitat at the European level and may be impacted by future climate change.

Slacks and related wetlands are arguably our most precious habitat for dune plants, holding a high diversity of species and about 43% of the 'notable' dune plants. Ongoing research at the Devil's Hole, Ravenmeols, identified 174 species in its developing slacks by 2020. They included several rarities, including Flat-sedge which is reckoned to be one of the most rapidly declining plants in Britain and is Red-listed as 'vulnerable'. My survey in 2008 showed that Flat-sedge was well-established in the dunes, favouring waterlogged, young calcareous dune-slacks, with an estimated population size of 15-20,000 individuals. However, a repeat of the study a decade later revealed a 17% decline in colony size, probably due to competition from dense vegetation. Some slacks develop tall-fen vegetation, an interesting component of which is Blunt-flowered Rush. Uncommon in the Northwest, this plant is more typical of the East Anglian fens. I conducted a coastwide survey of the rush in 2013, finding 18 spreading patches in only six wet dune-slacks. The Devil's Hole has two patches, one of which appeared in 2020.

Although most slack plants are adapted to non-saline conditions, a few are more often associated with saltmarshes, being found mainly in the younger slacks near the shore. Examples include Saltmarsh Rush, Sea Club-rush, Sea Milkwort and Sea Arrowgrass. As slacks mature, they become less maritime in character, salt-adapted plants gradually disappearing. This trend is particularly well seen in the younger stages of the Green Beach north of Ainsdale-on-Sea where the proportion of saltmarsh species in the flora declined rapidly over the first four years of slack development.

Flooded dune-slack in winter, Ainsdale Sandhills Local Nature Reserve

One of the most abundant slack plants is Creeping Willow, occurring here mostly as the highly variable coastal variety *argentea*. The catkins are an important source of nectar and pollen for spring-flying insects. Although it usually grows close to the ground, Creeping Willow can sometimes reach 3 m in height. E.D. McNicholl (1883) described it eloquently as:

"The little grey *salix* the foliage of which often shines with silvery lustre…. Very pretty in the early summer, are the innumerable catkins; and a few weeks later, when the ripe cottony seed is discharged, most curious is the spectacle, the quantity being so vast as often to be gathered up by the eddying wind in what, but for the season, might be taken for snow drifts."

Creeping Willow usually appears within about 10 years of a slack being formed and may eventually become dominant, little other than mosses growing under its dense canopy in the oldest wet-slacks. It can also spread onto the lower parts of fixed-dunes. Rabbits browse the stems and seem able to control it to some extent, at least in younger slacks.

Some slack plants are closely associated with Creeping Willow. One is the increasingly rare Yellow Bird's-nest, a strange looking, biscuit-coloured plant with scale-like leaves, lacking green pigment (chlorophyll). It obtains

Creeping Willow male catkins, Ravenmeols

its food from the breakdown of soil organic matter, via the activity of a fungus in its roots. Another is one of Sefton's specialities, Round-leaved Wintergreen, whose beautiful, white, waxy, saucer-shaped flowers can be found commonly in suitable habitat throughout the dunes. This plant is listed as 'nationally scarce', being mainly restricted to west-coast dunes from Cumbria to Devon.

Grass-of-Parnassus is an iconic slack plant that has attracted attention since the early 19th century. Not a grass at all, but related to the saxifrages, its starry, white flowers can be found in late summer, especially around the dryer fringes of wet-slacks, looking like a tidemark. Writing in 1883, E.D. McNicholl observed:

Round-leaved Wintergreen in flower, Ainsdale

"There are localities among the sandhills beyond Birkdale where, in favourable seasons, so vast is the quantity of the *Parnassia* that the whiteness of the ground may be compared to that given by daisies to the sward."

Declining nationally, Grass-of-Parnassus has been Red-listed as 'vulnerable' in England. However, the plant remains abundant in some Sefton Coast dune-slacks. It has also colonised Birkdale Green Beach since 2004. A coastwide volunteer survey of its distribution in 2013 recorded over 46,000 flowering plants, one of the largest populations in Britain. They were concentrated mainly in younger slacks, especially in areas with shorter vegetation maintained by Rabbit-grazing or light trampling.

A flowering plant of Grass-of-Parnassus, Birkdale Green Beach

Abundant Grass-of-Parnassus at Cabin Hill NNR in 2008

The marsh/spotted-orchid group is particularly associated with slacks. Four species occur here, together with several hybrids. By far the commonest is the Early Marsh-orchid, most plants being of the brick-red, coastal subspecies *coccinea*, which is endemic to Britain. There is also a very rare white variety. Described as looking like '*a fat little hyacinth*', this lovely flower can appear in colonies numbering thousands. Much less frequent, but apparently increasing on the coast, are the magenta spikes of the Southern Marsh-orchid, sometimes reaching heights of 50 cm. Its close relative, the Northern Marsh-orchid, is shorter and darker and has a more restricted distribution in the dunes. Its largest populations occur on the ranges of Altcar Training Camp.

Another orchid of the slacks is the Marsh Helleborine which, despite being Red-listed as 'near threatened' in England, often occurs here in spectacular numbers. Unlike most other helleborines, it has particularly attractive flowers; but arguably even more beautiful is

its rare pale variety *ochroleuca*. Tragically, the Fragrant Orchid seems to be extinct here. I last saw it in 1988 on Ainsdale NNR and Formby Golf Course. Could it turn up again? Another slack plant that has disappeared in modern times is the Marsh Lousewort. Red-listed as 'vulnerable' this species was known in one Birkdale LNR slack up to the mid-1990s but Joshua Styles and I searched for it in June 2018 and failed to rediscover the plant. It must therefore be presumed extinct.

Early Marsh-orchid (coastal form) (left) and Southern Marsh-orchid (right)

Marsh Helleborine variety *ochroleuca*, Cabin Hill NNR

Marsh Helleborine, Devil's Hole, Ravenmeols

Younger slacks with short, open vegetation are favoured by low-growing species like the Bog Pimpernel whose exquisite pink flowers can form extensive carpets. Knotted Pearlwort has a similar stature, with small star-shaped, white flowers. These two are often accompanied by yellowish-green tufts of Small-fruited Yellow-sedge, which has a mainly northern and western British distribution. My coastwide survey of this sedge in 2016 found a total of 7300 plants in 44 colonies, the largest of these being in the Devil's Hole blowout. It occurred mostly in areas of young calcareous slack vegetation. There was a strong association with disturbed sites where the vegetation height was lowered, as in Natterjack Toad scrapes and slacks impacted by vehicles or human trampling. About half the sites showed evidence of Rabbit grazing.

Bog Pimpernel, Devil's Hole, Ravenmeols

Small-fruited Yellow-sedge, Devil's Hole

Often growing with the yellow-sedge is the attractive Seaside Centaury, here near its northern limit on the west coast and rated 'nationally scarce'. The closely related Lesser Centaury also likes recently-formed slacks. There are drifts of this regionally notable plant on parts of Birkdale Green Beach, together with another species of conservation importance, the Strawberry Clover, so-called because its (inedible) seed-heads resemble pale-pink strawberries. Another important slack plant is the Variegated Horsetail. Although frequent in many of the older slacks and scrapes, it is easily overlooked. This species has a largely northern and western distribution in Britain and was recently described as being "Vanishingly rare in lowland England." Also found in scrapes is the Lesser Water-plantain. Red-listed as 'vulnerable' in England, this is a nationally declining species due to loss and overgrowth of small water-bodies. During a 2011 survey, Patricia Lockwood and I counted 422 plants at 13 sites in the dunes, all being artificially deepened scrapes or ponds. Although this study has not been repeated, casual observations suggest we have lost sites for Lesser Water-plantain over the last decade. The distinctive Yellow Bartsia has a restricted distribution on the coast, being mainly seen on the edges of wetlands in the Cabin Hill area and in Ainsdale NNR. It seems to respond well to disturbance by livestock, 20,000 flower-spikes being estimated in Ainsdale's Dune Restoration Area in 2004.

Seaside Centaury, Hightown dunes

Yellow Bartsia, Cabin Hill NNR

Variegated Horsetail, Hightown dunes

The declining status of another wetland plant, Tubular Water-dropwort, prompted a survey in 2009. I counted 1280 plants in five duneland localities, mostly in drains, ditches or scrapes where the ground surface had been lowered by human activity, thereby creating wetter conditions. Due to the effects of nutrient enrichment and reduction in grazing, this species is Red-listed as 'vulnerable' in England.

The most restricted of our slack plants is the regionally 'notable' Black Bog-rush, occurring as a single individual at Birkdale LNR. When the late Neil Robinson and I found it in 1977 as a new vice-county record, it formed a clump 30 cm across. It is still there but now has a diameter of 1.5 m. As its nearest locality is in North Wales, there was speculation that this plant may have been introduced, though by whom, why and when is a mystery.

Tubular Water-dropwort, New Green Beach drain pond

The 2020 *Inventory of Vascular Plants for the Sefton Coast* included 470 non-native or introduced native plants for the sand-dunes, about 38% of the flora. In 2020, I published a 20-year study of duneland aliens, finding that their proportion had increased steadily since 1999, especially in scrub/woodland habitat and disturbed ground. Between 2005 and 2018, twice as many new non-natives than native plants were found. It seemed that the relatively open habitats of coastal dunes were particularly susceptible to alien plant invasions.

Twenty-four of our non-native plants show invasive characteristics and have a significant impact on the ecology of the dunes; fortunately, however, most aliens are relatively benign. By far the greatest damage has been caused by Sea Buckthorn, a plant that is native on the east coast of Britain but not here. It was introduced by the manorial estates in the 1890s to reduce sand-blow and to create hedges to exclude trespassers. It quickly forms dense spiny stands several metres tall, eliminating most other plants. As it has the ability to fix nitrogen in root nodules, this shrub enriches the soil, making it less suitable for duneland flora. Several of our rarest dune plants are threatened by its spread. At the time of writing (2021), some of the largest patches of Sea Buckthorn are at Ravenmeols, with seven clumps totalling about 0.9 ha, while on Southport Marine Lake dunes, two enormous stands have a total area of around 0.8 ha.

Other deliberate introductions are the invasive poplars, Balm-of-Gilead, Grey and White, together with several species of pine, especially Corsican and Lodgepole. However, most exotics have appeared as accidental releases from cultivation, as garden-escapes or through trading links with other countries.

Fruiting Sea Buckthorn, Birkdale Common

Japanese Rose invading Hightown dunes

Other known invasives that can pose problems include Japanese Knotweed and its even larger hybrid relative, Bohemian Knotweed. These are quite widespread along the coast, especially on road-sides but are now being controlled by the relevant land-owners. Another familiar garden-escape is the rampant Russian Vine or 'mile-a-minute plant', fortunately found in only a few places as yet. The densely spiny Japanese Rose, with either pink or white flowers, is rapidly increasing. It is highly invasive on the Danish and German dunes where it can reach 100% ground-cover. A coastwide volunteer survey in 2014 measured 600 patches of the shrub covering 6 ha, equivalent to about eight football pitches. A separate study of larger bushes at Birkdale showed they were growing at over 20% per annum, doubling in size every four or five years. Recent research shows that Japanese Rose alters dune soils, which may hinder recovery of vegetation after removal of the shrub. Despite its known impacts nationally and internationally, this pest-plant is still widely advertised, recommended on television gardening programmes and sold in garden centres.

Another potential problem is Broad-leaved Everlasting-pea, which started to spread rapidly at Ainsdale and Birkdale LNRs in about 2012. Like other members of its family, it has the ability to fix atmospheric nitrogen and therefore increase soil fertility. Smaller garden-escapes include Snow-in-summer and White Stonecrop, both of which infest the dunes at Kenilworth Road, Ainsdale and turn up in lesser quantity elsewhere. The dreaded New Zealand Pigmy-weed, an aquarists' introduction, has invaded ponds and other wetlands all over the country. Fortunately, it has been found on relatively few occasions on the Sefton Coast and has been controlled with herbicides or, in two cases, by infilling ponds. The vivid blue flowers of Green Alkanet are a familiar sight in spring and summer along the edges of tracks and in open woodland but this shows no signs of being invasive.

Broad-leaved Everlasting-pea increasing on Birkdale frontal dunes

Green Alkanet, Wick's Path, Formby Point

The most familiar member of the alien flora to the general public is the evening-primrose, sometimes known as the 'dusk-beacon' because the blooms open in the evening and are pollinated by moths. Its gaudy yellow flower-spikes, a metre or more high, adorn the older mobile and fixed-dunes from early July to the first frosts. There are six main kinds on the coast, three being hybrids. All of them can be found on Crosby Coastal Park, where the colourful hybrid between the Large-flowered and Small-flowered (*Oenothera ×britannica*) is especially numerous. Evening-primroses mainly come from the Americas, being grown in Britain as ornamental plants in 1629. At first, their roots were eaten, cultivation for the familiar medicinal oil coming much later. One suggestion is that the Sefton Coast plants were introduced in ships importing cotton to Liverpool in the 19th century, the first record for the dunes being in 1801. Despite their abundance, evening-primroses do not represent a threat to the dune flora.

Another spectacular non-native plant is Hungarian Mullein with tall spikes of candelabra-like yellow flowers. A native of Eastern Europe, this plant was new to the Northwest of England when I found it in a woodland glade at Ravenmeols in 2011. A similarly unexpected find in 2009 was Small Nightshade spotted by Peter Brash growing on a Rabbit warren near the National Trust office at Formby. A great rarity in Britain with only 14 modern 10 km-square records, this distinctive annual was still present in 2017 when my survey, with friends, located 62 plants near to the original discovery. Yet another alien surprise was Four-leaved Pink-sorrel of the variety 'Iron Cross' found by Patricia Lockwood on the Green Beach strandline at Ainsdale in May 2019. This was only the second vice-county record of a plant mostly seen in Greater London. It was still there the following year.

Hybrid Evening-primrose *Oenothera ×britannica*, Crosby Coastal Park

Well-drained soils, combined with summer drought, suit the lifestyle of spring bulbs. From February to May, an amazing variety of well-known garden species is seen from snowdrops to crocuses, grape-hyacinths and various squills. Patricia Lockwood spotted a superb specimen of Summer Snowflake at Wicks Lake, Formby, in 2013. It has been seen each year since. Also abundant are the daffodils, represented by a remarkable range of different cultivars. The early-flowering bulbs are soon replaced by Garden Tulips and then by white-flowered clumps of Star-of-Bethlehem. The related Drooping Star-of-Bethlehem is much rarer, occurring only at Larkhill woods.

Small Nightshade, Formby Point

Four-leaved Pink-sorrel 'Iron Cross', Ainsdale beach

Early Crocus, Kenilworth Road dunes, Ainsdale

Summer Snowflake, Wicks Lake, Formby

Hungarian Mullein, Ravenmeols (left) and Drooping Star-of-Bethlehem, Larkhill (right)

Willow-leaved Cotoneaster, Formby Point

Also in shady places, Lily-of-the-valley can be abundant. Bluebells put on a fine display but the native species is now rare, having been replaced by the less welcome hybrid with Spanish Bluebell, which comes in a range of colour-forms. Summer drought also favours non-native succulent plants, such as Cypress Spurge and various garden stonecrops. That familiar, berry-bearing, garden shrub, cotoneaster, spreads into the dunes through birds eating the berries. Sixteen different kinds have been identified here, often a long way from the nearest garden. Fortunately, they don't seem to be invasive here.

Not surprisingly, there is a close relationship between the frequency of introduced plants and a site's proximity to housing. One reason is the deliberate dumping of garden refuse, which is commonplace all along the coast. Thus, Sally Edmondson's survey of the National Trust's boundary with housing at Formby revealed over 60 tips of garden waste on National Trust land. She wrote: "Gardeners who take a pride in producing beautiful surroundings to their houses can pose a very real threat to the quality of semi-natural habitats on the other side of their garden fence." The same is true almost everywhere. Not only does this fly-tipping lead to alien introductions, but it also adds nutrients to dune soils, resulting in the loss of typical sand-dune plants and their replacement by nutrient-demanding species, such as Common Nettle.

While over 90% of the introduced plants are relatively innocuous, a small number is actually or potentially invasive. Several of these have already been highlighted. Others that may give rise to concern for the future are Traveller's-joy, an introduced native spreading rapidly in the Birkdale frontal dunes, Cypress Spurge at Hightown and Michaelmas-daisy and Canadian Goldenrod almost everywhere.

Invasive Canadian Goldenrod at Hightown dunes

HYBRIDS

An increasing interest in hybrids led to as many as 119 being recorded in the sand-dunes by 2020. Many plants hybridise quite readily, some of the progeny being rare and of conservation interest. For example, three of the 15 hybrid willows on the Sefton Coast are 'nationally rare'. Most frequent of the three is Creeping Willow × Osier. I have logged and measured more than 500 bushes of this hybrid in the dunes. Over 120 of them grow in the Devil's Hole at Ravenmeols, an extraordinary concentration bearing in mind that the plant is known from only a handful of other British localities, where it is mostly rare. The British endemic triple hybrid Creeping Willow × Osier × Grey Willow is much harder to identify and only a few bushes have been found here. The third rarity and the only one with an English name is Don's Willow (Creeping Willow × Purple Willow), represented by 40 individuals widely distributed along the coast, mainly in slacks. With striking red-tinged catkins in spring, fiery red stems and neat, bluish-green leaves, this hybrid is particularly distinctive. Although its parents are relatively common, it is one of the rarest British plants, only three or four bushes being known away from the Sefton Coast.

Don's Willow with male catkins, Lifeboat Road, Formby

Two more very rare hybrids both involve the Baltic Rush as one of the parents, the others being Hard Rush and Soft Rush. The tallest rush in Britain, Baltic Rush × Hard Rush is endemic to this country and has been recorded 'in the wild' three times on the Sefton Coast. Its only other locality is at Lytham St. Anne's LNR, Lancashire. The smaller Baltic Rush × Soft Rush is known only from the Sefton Coast, where it has also been found three times, and from one site in Germany. Both these hybrids have been cultivated and transplanted to wetlands along the coast to save them from extinction.

Mike Wilcox investigating the tall Baltic Rush × Hard Rush hybrid at Birkdale

Southern Marsh-orchid × Common Spotted-orchid, Birkdale Green Beach

Common Spotted x Early Marsh-orchid, Birkdale Green Beach

The marsh-orchids also produce hybrids, their parentage taxing the keenest botanist. Most often seen is *Dactylorhiza* ×*grandis*, a strongly-marked cross between Common Spotted-orchid and Southern Marsh-orchid. Much rarer in the dunes is a spectacular hybrid between Common Spotted and the coastal form of Early Marsh-orchid, which I have seen only once.

Intermediate Centaury is beautiful and distinctive plant derived from interbreeding between Common and Seaside Centauries. Although it occurs quite widely in the Sefton dunes, this is its only locality in the country. For various reasons, including the fact that it breeds true, it has recently been reclassified as a full species.

The 'nationally rare' Intermediate Centaury, Devil's Hole, Ravenmeols

SOME SPECIAL PLANTS

Isle of Man Cabbage

Occurring only in Britain, the 'nationally scarce' Isle of Man Cabbage has bright-yellow, four-petalled flowers and distinctive grey-green deeply divided leaves. It is mainly found near the sea on open dunes in north-west England, south-west Scotland and South Wales. This plant has been found growing wild in three places on the Sefton Coast: Blundellsands, Birkdale frontal dunes and the dunes west of Southport Marine Lake. The first of these colonies was long-established but its habitat was progressively destroyed by housing development until, by 1989, the plant was confined to a sandy footpath at Park Drive, Blundell-sands. The Birkdale site was an eroded hollow that I discovered in 1983. Here, the cabbage population increased from 55 individuals in 1983 to 168 in 1986, but then declined to extinction by 1993, due to invasion by Sea Buckthorn. In 1989, my friends Richard Hall and Deborah Nissenbaum found the Marine Lake colony, consisting of 347 plants. It increased to 874 individuals in 1997 but then declined until none was found in 2012. Surprisingly, a few plants reappeared here in 2015 and this small population has persisted.

The Park Drive colony was lost in 1992 when the footpath was top-soiled and turfed over. However, a rescue operation organised by the Lancashire Wildlife Trust and Sefton Ranger Service moved 385 small plants to two suitable sand-dune sites nearby, at Hall Road and Crosby Marine Park. Despite over 90% mortality in the first year, populations eventually became well-established. Then, in 2011, the dune ridge occupied by the Crosby colony was used as a source of sand for a coast defence scheme at Hightown, appar-

Isle of Man Cabbage from transplant in 2011, Crosby Coastal Park

ently destroying this population. But no; the following year, hundreds of plants appeared on both the flattened ridge at Crosby and the sand deposited at Hightown, presumably from previously buried seed. Two small colonies were also created by emergency transplantation by volunteers of first-year plants and seed to new sites at Crosby and Birkdale. My most recent survey in 2015 with Patricia Lockwood found the total number of Isle of Man Cabbage plants on the Sefton Coast had increased to 2317, probably the largest population in Britain and therefore in the world.

Isle of Man Cabbage seems to thrive in rather thinly vegetated dunes with plenty of bare sand and evidently tolerates severe disturbance. These conditions can be maintained by moderately heavy pedestrian trampling and Rabbit grazing but, because of widespread overgrowth of rank grasses and scrub, much of the duneland is now unsuitable for this plant.

Isle of Man Cabbage volunteer rescue operation, Crosby Coastal Park, August 2011

Baltic Rush

This medium-sized, patch-forming rush is relatively easy to recognise in the field from its stiff, glossy, dark-green shoots and chocolate-brown flower-heads. In Britain, Baltic Rush is a 'nationally scarce' plant of sand-dune slacks and other damp areas in sand, mud or peat near the sea. It is mainly found on the north and north-east coasts of Scotland and the Hebrides, the only English locality being a small area of the Birkdale Sandhills where it was discovered by R.S. Adamson in 1913. By 1944, the rush had disappeared from Adamson's site but had already spread to new ones. In 1969/70, Clive Stace found it in only three Birkdale slacks, predicting its extinction "in the fairly near future". Luckily, this did not happen and the rush actually prospered in the 1970s. When I surveyed it in 1981/82, the plant had spread to 10 slacks formed by wind-erosion at the northern end of Birkdale Sandhills. It continued to do well at Birkdale during the 1980s and early 1990s but, by 1997, it was clearly in decline at its northernmost sites, mainly due to the growth of Sea Buckthorn scrub.

Another survey in 2004 revealed that the plant had indeed disappeared from six slacks at the northern end of the Birkdale frontal dunes and from one site on the Royal Birkdale Golf Course but had colonised three new slacks and the Birkdale Green Beach to the south of its previous range. There had been some losses but the area occupied by the rush had increased 34% since 1982.

I monitored the rush again in 2015 with Patricia Lockwood. Despite severe damage to its largest colony by illegal off-road driving, the total area of patches had increased almost three-fold. We concluded that this species is a good coloniser of young, sparsely vegetated wet-slacks and may then persist for some years, before declining as the habitat becomes dryer and more heavily vegetated. However, it is very vulnerable to scrub invasion and the spread of tall plants, such as Common Reed. As a 'northern' plant it might also be susceptible to climate change.

Baltic Rush in flower, Birkdale

Sharp Club-rush

Sharp Club-rush is 'nationally rare', having been recorded from only two British localities - in Jersey, where it has not been seen since the early 1970s, and the Sefton Coast sand-dunes. Why this species is so scarce in Britain is a mystery, as it is one of the World's most widely distributed wetland plants. It was originally found in 1909 by W.G. Travis at Massam's Slack in what is now Ainsdale NNR but it took him 19 years to identify it. Travis concluded that the colony was native but this has been debated ever since and it is just possible that the plant was introduced. The Massam's colony was extinct by 1978 but had already been taken into cultivation and transplanted to a pond near the Ainsdale reserve office, where it survived to the early 1990s. Using the cultivated stock, Dave Simpson transplanted it again in 1990 to four scrapes in the Birkdale frontal dunes where it flourished. Remarkably, Dan Wrench came across a patch on Birkdale Green Beach in 1999, where it must have spread naturally from one of the transplant sites. I studied the colonies at Birkdale in June 2004, finding five discrete patches of the plant the largest being the one recorded by Dan. In 2011, I was pleased to discover a new colony on the Green Beach. My most recent survey in 2014 showed the plant was doing well with a 171% increase since 2004.

Sharp Club-rush, Birkdale frontal dunes

Dune Helleborine

A less than visually attractive but fascinating orchid, the Dune Helleborine is 'nationally scarce' and endemic to Britain. Apart from a few inland populations, it is restricted to dunelands in Anglesey, Merseyside, Lancashire and Cumbria. On the Sefton Coast, it often grows with the superficially similar Green-flowered Helleborine, the latter having drooping flowers that hardly open. Peter Gateley surveyed both of them in 1988 and 1992, recording an increase of Dune Helleborine from 870 to 1911 flower-spikes and of Green-flowered Helleborine from 263 to 624. He noted that the Dune Helleborine was particularly associated with Creeping Willow; it was also found under deciduous trees and shrubs, in pine plantations, on open fixed-dunes and in disturbed areas, such as along fence-lines and the edges of footpaths. He considered threats to its future were the over-stabilisation of dunes, including the development of tall-grass swards, scrub encroachment and soil enrichment.

Although there was no evidence of a decline, another detailed survey of this special plant was long overdue and funding was found to organise one in the summers of 2008 and 2009. About 30 volunteers, led by Pauline Michell, covered most of the dune area, finding and mapping 7146 Dune and 1543 Green-flowered Helleborines, a big increase on previous surveys, perhaps partly due to better coverage. The largest populations were found on Ainsdale NNR and the National Trust's Formby Point estate. Wet summers in 2007 and 2008 seem to have suited the helleborines, especially in the drought-prone pine plantations where the highest numbers were logged. At the time, these counts were the largest in Britain (and therefore in the world), giving us a particular responsibility for the conservation of Dune Helleborine.

Dune Helleborine, Ainsdale

Early Sand-grass

Officially listed as 'nationally rare' and 'near threatened' in England, the Early Sand-grass was discovered on dunes at Southport Marine Lake in 1996 by Dave Earl and Joyce Buckley-Earl. Its diminutive stature, only about an inch (2 cm) tall, together with its early flowering season in February and March, may be why it had not been found before on the Sefton Coast. I mapped its distribution on the Marine Lake dunes in 1999 when it covered nearly 1500 square metres; five years on, in March 2004, the colony had increased in area by 47%. Catherine Highfield and Patricia Lockwood joined me for another survey in 2011, recording a further 40% increase, so that the area covered by the plant had more than doubled since 1999. Most of the population is close to a low dune ridge which forms a 'bulge' jutting out into the Marine Lake on its western side. The plant seems to like a very open sparsely vegetated surface. At Southport, the habitat is maintained by a slow rain of blown sand from the adjacent foreshore together with locally intense human trampling and a little Rabbit-grazing. Unfortunately, its habitat is now threatened by spreading Sea Buckthorn and Japanese Rose.

Early Sand-grass colouring the ground pink on Southport Marine Lake dunes

Dune Wormwood

Perhaps our most spectacular botanical discovery was back in 2004 when Mike Wilcox and I found a low growing plant we didn't recognise on the dunes at Crosby Coastal Park. A small sample was sent away for identification and it turned out to be a coastal subspecies of the very rare Field Wormwood. At first it was thought to be a new plant for Britain, being known only from dunes between southern Spain and Belgium. We debated whether it might have been introduced but the eminent botanist, Eric Clement, argued it should be considered native and recommended the new English name 'Dune Wormwood', which was adopted by the Botanical Society of Britain & Ireland. Then we discovered the plant was also known from a dune system in South Wales, Crymlyn Warren, providing further evidence for its native status. However, the Welsh population soon became extinct, being later re-introduced to Crymlyn using the same stock. One specimen was still "hanging on" there in 2021. The original Crosby plant produced five offspring and, by 2020, was over five metres across. Because of its relative vulnerability, cuttings were taken by Joshua Styles, under license, for propagation by the *North West Rare Plant Initiative*.

Botanical Society of Britain & Ireland visiting the Dune Wormwood at Crosby Coastal Park

Field Gentian

One of the most rapidly declining British plants and Red-listed as 'endangered' in England, the beautiful Field Gentian is now largely restricted to the Sefton dunes in our region. It has been known here for over 180 years but has become mostly confined to the Ainsdale NNR and LNR in recent decades.

In the early 2000s, it was noticed that numbers of Field Gentian were really taking off in an area of Ainsdale Sand Dunes NNR where pine trees and scrub had been cleared and sheep-grazing introduced a few years earlier (the 'Dune Restoration Area'). By 2009, it was thought desirable to clarify the plant's status, so Patricia Lockwood and I searched about 100 ha of open dunes in the northern and western parts of the reserve. We counted an impressive total of 140,700 Field Gentians, mostly in dry and damp slacks, 65% being in the Dune Restoration Area. There were also enormous numbers of the closely related Autumn Gentian, another declining species that is 'near threatened' in England. Unfortunately, we didn't have time to count those. Almost all the Field Gentians were in compartments fenced for winter-grazing by sheep but it was clear that year-round Rabbit-grazing was also important to its success, giving important insights into ways of conserving this species. The Ainsdale NNR population is one of the largest in Britain and is probably of European significance. Smaller colonies have also been found in the slacks of Ainsdale Sandhills LNR but not recently in other parts of the dunes.

Field Gentian, Ainsdale NNR

Autumn Gentian, Ainsdale NNR

am often asked where and when to go to see particular plants. While interesting species can occur almost anywhere, some places are better than others and, of course, it's important to know when the target plant is likely to be in flower. A little knowledge can save a lot of time searching large areas at the wrong time of year. I have described several of the key sites below with an emphasis on areas with easy access. The Merseyrail train service links most of the coast, stations at regular intervals connecting with a coastal footpath and cycle-way. There is also a series of carparks, mostly pay-and-

display, though these can often be full in summer. Access on foot is permitted to most of the dune system, the only exceptions being a few areas fenced for grazing by livestock on the nature reserves. Guided wildflower walks are often arranged by voluntary bodies or site managers and may be advertised online. The usual safety precautions apply, especially if visiting the area alone. It goes without saying that plant material should not be collected without permission of the landowner and Natural England.

Marshside

The extensive, recently formed saltmarshes between Marshside and Southport provide a rich assortment of plants typical of this tidal habitat. Saltings between Fairway and Hesketh Road have the greatest potential, with increasing populations of Common and Lax-flowered Sea-lavender, together with their rare hybrid. In full flower during August, their deep purple hues contrast with the swathes of paler-flowered Sea Aster. Visits in September

and October are recommended for other saltmarsh plants, including four species of glasswort, which colour up in autumn. Also at this time, the annual orache species and hybrids achieve their full stature and bear the fruits needed for identification. It is essential to check the tide-tables before visiting the saltmarsh. It is safest to go out on a falling tide and avoid drainage creeks.

A field visit to study Sea-lavenders on the saltings at Marshside

Southport Marine Lake dunes

The narrow strip of dunes on the western side of the Marine Lake is renowned for two special plants, the 'nationally rare' Early Sand-grass and British endemic Isle of Man Cabbage. The 'smallest grass in the world' flowers in March and early April, being almost impossible to find later in the year when it dies down completely. It is abundant on sandy east-facing slopes, especially to the north of the 'bulge' of dunes that sticks out into the lake. However its favoured habitat is being invaded by Sea Buckthorn and Japanese Rose. Now much reduced in number, Isle of Man Cabbage plants are best searched for when they are in flower from late May to July. They may be discovered alongside sandy paths on the crest of the main north/south ridge or on the 'bulge' A variety of typical coastal flowers, including many spring-flowering dune annuals, can also be found, especially on the flatter ground nearer the lake, which is grazed by an unusual combination of Rabbits and Canada Geese.

Flower-rich fixed dunes, grazed by Rabbits and geese, Southport Marine Lake

Queen's Jubilee Nature Trail

Popular with dog-walkers, this relict area of dunes on the southern outskirts of Southport has a surprisingly diverse flora, well over 200 species of flowering plants and ferns having been identified. The wet-slack areas in the centre of the site are worth exploring in high summer for species such as Marsh Helleborine and Flat-sedge, a large population of the latter being discovered during a 2015 survey. Dune Helleborines are also present, flowering in July. Parts of the site have been heavily colonised by Sea Buckthorn and Japanese Rose, which are gradually being controlled. The many willows include one of the best selections of rare hybrids on the coast.

Queen's Jubilee Nature Trail in a wet winter

Birkdale frontal dunes (north) and Birkdale Green Beach

Take a path west from Selworthy Road, Birkdale, cross the coast road (with care) and explore the strip of frontal dunes and slacks to the north and south. From May to August, a wealth of wildflowers can be seen, including some major rarities. The first slack you enter

Pond with Sharp Club-rush, Birkdale frontal dunes

Birkdale frontal dunes slack with dark-green patches of Baltic Rush

has abundant Flat-sedge and a fine display of Yellow Iris (best in May/June); turn right and walk about 400 m north to find Sharp Club-rush growing around a circular pond, or left to a slack that supports the largest population of Baltic Rush on the coast. The southern end of this slack has a mixed stand of Greater Pond-sedge and Brown Sedge. All the slacks have plenty of marsh-orchids, Marsh Helleborines and Grass-of-Parnassus, the latter not flowering until August.

A footpath alongside the ditch from the Baltic Rush slack leads to Tagg's Island – a dune ridge enclosing a large reed-bed. The south-west corner has a fine stand of translocated Sharp Club-rush. A variety of horsetails along the eastern edge of the marsh includes the hybrid Shore Horsetail.

To the west of Tagg's Island lies the central section of Birkdale Green Beach. Finding a route through the dense growths of Alder and marshy fen can be tricky but it is worth seeking out paths created by dog-walkers to look for Wild Celery and Parsley Water-dropwort in the fen, while beyond the last row of Alders, Small patches of Saltmarsh Flat-sedge and drifts of Seaside and Lesser Centaury are well worth the effort. There are also a few patches of Baltic Rush on the upper saltmarsh, interspersed with Sea Rush and Saltmarsh Rush Sea Milkwort flowers in spectacular abundance in June, while masses of Strawberry Clover, Red-listed as 'vulnerable' in Great Britain, are equally impressive a little later.

Tagg's Island Reedbed, Birkdale Green Beach

Lesser Centaury, Birkdale Green Beach

Strawberry Clover, Birkdale Green Beach

In late July/early August, it is well worth walking about 500 m north to see a fantastic display of flowering Parsley Water-dropwort, turning the marsh white; a pretty good show for a plant Red-listed as 'near threatened' in England.

Parsley Water-dropwort, Birkdale Green Beach

New and Newest Green Beaches

Accessed via Ainsdale beach, the southern extensions of Birkdale Green Beach, named the 'New Green Beach' and 'Newest Green Beach', originated in 2004 and 2008 respectively. Each consists of an embryo/mobile dune ridge with a developing slack to the rear. The slacks, in particular, support a diverse, rapidly changing flora, including a rich mix of species adapted to both saline and fresh-water conditions. By autumn 2019, about 250 plants had been identified on the older New Green Beach, specialities including a large population of Grass-of-Parnassus (August) and several large patches of Slender Spike-rush, together with abundant Lesser Water-parsnip and Parsley Water-dropwort (May-July). Mainly found along the slack edges in June and July, are masses of Southern Marsh-orchids, Early Marsh-orchids and Marsh Helleborines. These orchids have recently colonised the Newest Green Beach, together with Grass-of-Parnassus. The drain outfall at the northern end of the New Green Beach has a fine stand of Tubular Water-dropwort (May-June), while the adjacent Green Beach wet-slack has one of the best colonies of Variegated Horsetail on the coast.

'Newest Green Beach' slack in summer

Early Marsh-orchids, 'Newest Green Beach'

Southern Birkdale frontal dunes and slacks

To the west and north of Sands Lake, Ainsdale, is a fascinating area of floristically diverse dunes and slacks, the latter having mostly formed by wind erosion as recently as the early/mid 1970s. Thanks to the energetic efforts of volunteers, this area has largely been cleared of invasive Sea Buckthorn thickets in recent years, allowing the native flora to thrive. This includes large populations of Pyramidal and Bee Orchids, the latter occurring in spectacular numbers on ridges towards the shore in early June. Dune Helleborine is also well represented in July, especially on the fringes of willow patches in the damper hollows. Small slacks south-west of the lake have dense patches of Blunt-flowered Rush, while more careful searches may reveal Adder's-tongue fern (June-July). The larger wet-slacks have plenty of marsh-orchids (May-June), Marsh Helleborine (July) and Grass-of-Parnassus (August), while the long, narrow slack 170 m northwest of the lake is especially rich, supporting stands of Flat-sedge, Slender Spike-rush, Brown Sedge and Variegated Horsetail (June-August).

Round-leaved Wintergreen is common throughout the area. A more adventurous explorer venturing about 750 m north of Sands Lake may locate a patch of Baltic Rush (the southernmost on the coast) at the western end of a wet-slack, while the eastern section supports impressive plants of Greater Tussock-sedge at its only Sefton locality. Sands Lake itself has fringing beds of Grey Club-rush. Towards the northern end of the lake the attractive flowers of Bogbean appear in early May, followed in early June by the occasional Greater Spearwort, looking like a giant buttercup and masses of Yellow Iris. This walk can also be combined with the New and Newest Green Beaches to the west (see above).

Birkdale frontal dunes slack in winter

Greater Tussock Sedge with Yellow Iris, Birkdale frontal dunes slack

Bogbean in flower at
Sands Lake, Ainsdale

Ainsdale Sandhills Local Nature Reserve

A short stroll south from the Ainsdale Discovery Centre brings the plant enthusiast into one of the finest areas of dunes and slacks on the coast. Botanical riches on fixed-dune ridges in early summer include the superb Dune Pansy, sadly becoming increasingly scarce, accompanied by Portland Spurge, while the younger slacks are full of marsh-orchids, including hybrids difficult to name. There is an enormous population of Pyramidal Orchids (June-July) vying for attention with numerous Bee Orchids and sheets of Marsh Helleborines. In late summer, the largest slack has a few Field Gentians, while further south is a slack renowned for an enormous stand of the nationally rare and endemic Baltic Rush × Hard Rush hybrid, derived from a conservation transplant in 1992. The older slacks to the east should not be overlooked, the largest of these having extensive patches of Bogbean, Slender Tufted-sedge, Purple Moor-grass and Brown Sedge, best seen in May-June. As in many

Slack in Ainsdale LNR, with a large stand of hybrid Baltic Rush

other parts of the dune system, invasive Sea Buckthorn is a major problem but volunteers organised by *Gems in the Dunes* have been tackling it in recent years. Their efforts were augmented by *Green Sefton* in the 2020/21 winter, when several of the eastern slacks were cleared of scrub using heavy machinery.

Portland Spurge, Ainsdale LNR

Ainsdale Sand Dunes National Nature Reserve

This enormous reserve holds a cornucopia of botanical gems but many are situated in the 'Dune Restoration Area' which is at least 20 minutes walk from the nearest access point. One of the easier areas to get to is Pinfold Meadow, right next to the main entrance and bordering the railway line. This small former agricultural field is surprisingly rich in species over 100 higher plants having been recorded. It consists of a mosaic of acidic and neutral grassland with a damper area in the centre, the latter having the uncommon Narrow Buckler-fern. Open patches in the Rabbit-grazed area near the railway support a range of dune annuals, including the nationally declining Shepherd's-cress and also Changing Forget-me-not, whose flowers open yellow before turning blue. These two are at their best in late April or early May.

Changing Forget-me-not, Ainsdale NNR

Lesser Buckler-fern, Pinfold Meadow, Ainsdale NNR

Panoramic view of Ainsdale Sand Dunes National Nature Reserve

Freshfield Dune Heath Nature Reserve

On the southern fringe of Woodvale aerodrome, Freshfield Dune Heath was purchased by the Lancashire Wildlife Trust from the Ministry of Defence in 2004. The western section is open to the public, footpaths providing attractive circular walks through the heath and woodland. The sandy soil was blown off the dunes centuries ago, its present-day acidity favouring sheets of Heather, which flowers spectacularly in August, while Gorse blooms throughout the year but is especially prolific in April. The reserve's specialities include the early flowering and diminutive Bird's-foot on short, Rabbit-grazed grassland and the Pill Sedge, found in open areas of grassland or young Heather. Also noteworthy is a large population of Spring Sedge, best seen in late April in the so-called 'Hay Meadow', consisting of neutral grassland close to the airfield. The many excavated ponds on the reserve support a variety of wetland plants, including the regionally uncommon Whorl-grass.

Spring Sedge, Freshfield Dune Heath hay meadow

Devil's Hole, Ravenmeols

Arguably the most spectacular landscape feature on the coast, Devil's Hole is an enormous active blow-out in the Ravenmeols Local Nature Reserve, south of Formby. It began to form during the Second World War, possibly as a result of a bomb explosion, being subsequently enlarged by wind erosion to cover nearly 4 ha, the largest blow-out in the country. Slack vegetation began to colonise in 2003, my regular surveys with Patricia Lockwood monitoring a steady increase from 16 species in 2004 to 175 by 2020. About 30 of these are regionally or nationally notable, highlighting the site's botanical importance. A particular feature is an abundance of Grass-of-Parnassus in August/September but, from May to autumn, there is invariably something interesting to see, including up to 10 different orchids, Small-fruited Yellow-sedge and all the coast's centauries, including the rare Intermediate Centaury. Of more specialist interest are at least 15 willows, two being the nationally rare hybrids, Creeping Willow × Osier and Don's Willow.

Grass-of-Parnassus, the Devil's Hole, Ravenmeols

Altcar Training Camp

Being one of the busiest military establishments in the country, Altcar Training Camp has restricted public access. However, each year several guided walks are organised by the Altcar Conservation Advisory Group, with permission of the Camp authorities. Especially popular are those in May to see the spectacular flowering of Green-winged Orchids on the Shooting Ranges. Other orchids on the estate include Bee, Pyramidal, Dune Helleborine, Green-flowered Helleborine, Marsh Helleborine, Common Spotted, Northern, Southern and Early Marsh-orchid and Common Twayblade, these requiring visits in June/July. Many other interesting plants can be seen during these walks. They include Ragged Robin, Adder's-tongue, Quaking-grass and a variety of sedges, together with the coast's only bush of Spurge-laurel, probably bird-sown.

Guided walk to see Green-winged Orchids, Altcar Training Camp

Hightown dunes

Although a relatively small area and heavily modified by past human activity, Hightown dunes have many attractions for the botanist. They include several bushes of the nationally rare hybrid Don's Willow with bright red stems and red-tinged male catkins in late April. These are followed in May and June by the striking white flowers of Burnet Rose, while the Isle of Man Cabbage can be found on the frontal dunes and strandline. A little later, purple spikes of Viper's-bugloss feature on track-sides. Unmissable in June and July is the 'shingle' beach of water-worn house bricks with the spectacular Yellow Horned-poppy, as well as the succulent Rock Samphire, Sea Sandwort and Biting Stonecrop. A small reed-bed behind the shingle beach has Common Meadow-rue and large patches of Lesser and Greater Pond-sedge, while a nearby scrape holds a transplanted patch of the extremely rare Baltic Rush × Soft Rush hybrid. Careful searches of the frontal dunes north and south of the Sailing Club may locate colonies of Sea Bindweed, though the June flowers are rather hard to find. Superficially similar pink-and-white blooms of the coastal form of Hedge Bindweed are frequent in August on the inland edge of the big northern reed-bed.

Hightown dunes looking north towards the reed-bed and Altcar Training Camp

Hightown 'shingle' beach of water-worn house bricks

Sea Sandwort on Hightown shore

Crosby Coastal Park

From May onwards, the dune ridges either side of the promenade at Crosby Coastal Park support our largest population of Isle of Man Cabbage, this being accompanied, in places, by the scarce coastal form of Groundsel. It is worth visiting in June to see spectacular numbers of Common Broomrape parasitising Sea Holly on the dunes south of Crosby Baths. North of the brick pumping station, a careful search may locate a few plants of Dune Wormwood at one of only two British localities. It flowers in early September. Wet grassland near the small boating lake has a spectacular colony of Southern Marsh-orchid in June, while Slender Spike-rush grows closer to the water's edge, care being needed to distinguish it from the Common Spike-rush. The dune ridges and sandy grasslands near Crosby Baths hold a remarkable display of evening-primroses in mid-summer, at least three species and several confusing hybrids presenting an identification challenge. My favourite is *Oenothera* ×*britannica* with bright red stems and buds. The Park is also renowned for other non-native plants, in particular a remarkable variety of garden-escapes along the eastern boundary, keen botanists finding new ones almost every year. One to look out for is the rare, brilliant-blue Triplet Lily.

Southern Marsh-orchids, Crosby Coastal Park

Floral diversity Crosby Coastal Park

Common Broomrape (left) and Triplet Lily (right), Crosby Coastal Park

THREATS AND CONSERVATION

The idea that parts of the Sefton Coast might merit protection and conservation for flora fauna and amenity dates back only a hundred years or so. For centuries the duneland and saltmarshes were considered a hostile place, from which t was hard to make a living. Few people tried; 200 years ago Formby was a tiny village founded by the Vikings, while Southport consisted of about 20 fishermen's cottages. Land-uses consisted mainly of livestock grazing and fishing, with small-scale arable agriculture on the dune backlands. Rabbit-warrening had also been an important activity for several centuries, while parts of Formby Point were levelled by hand to create fields for asparagus growing. This filled n the slacks and destroyed the natural undulating land-form. The treeless, over-grazed landscape was quite unlike what we see today, with unstable dunes and blowing sand everywhere.

Former Asparagus field at Formby Point in snow, showing ridge-and-furrow

Most of the duneland was owned by the Formby and Weld-Blundell manorial estates, which struggled to tame this veritable wilderness, describing it in the early 20th century as 'unprofitable waste'. The estates began a large-scale programme of afforestation from the 1880s to the 1930s, the aims being to grow timber as an income and to create shelter for small-holdings. Conifer plantations eventually covered about 12% of the dune system between Ravenmeols and Ainsdale.

Another land-use change took place between 1873 and 1912 when seven major championship golf courses were laid out on the coast, some being internationally renowned. These occupy another 10% of the duneland, though most of the land-form remains intact.

Especially since the mid-nineteenth century and the coming of the railways, built development increased rapidly, the settlements of Southport, Ainsdale, Formby, Crosby and Bootle being constructed largely on sand-dunes, destroying at least half of their original extent.

Conifer plantation on dunes, Formby Point

Then, before and after the Second World War and up to the 1960s, another funding source for the estates was commercial sand-winning. This devastated large areas of duneland from Hightown to Ainsdale, weakening coastal defences to the extent that the local authorities eventually had to step in and use planning law to prevent it.

However, by the mid 20th century, the pendulum was beginning to shift, with an increasing recognition of the value of intact sand-dunes for coast protection, recreation and perhaps, above all, for wildlife and landscape conservation. As early as 1915, Ainsdale, Birkdale and Freshfield dunes appeared in a

89

short-list of potential nature reserves drawn up by Charles Rothschild, while in 1944 the influential Nature Reserves Investigation Committee placed Ainsdale on its list of the 22 top wildlife sites in Britain, the intention being that these sites would be priorities for protection as National Nature Reserves after the war. It took another 21 years of difficult negotiations with the Weld-Blundell estate before Ainsdale Sand Dunes NNR was finally purchased for the nation by the Nature Conservancy (now Natural England) in 1965. The National Trust acquired Formby Point two years later though its 'Enterprise Neptune' scheme. The Ribble Estuary and Cabin Hill NNRs followed in 1979 and 1984 respectively. From the early 1980s, other important dune areas at Ainsdale/Birkdale and Ravenmeols were protected by Sefton Council as Local Nature Reserves, while in 1985 the whole of the undeveloped coast was included in the Merseyside Green Belt. For purposes of planning, the local authority also recognised 24 Local Wildlife Sites in the coastal zone, several being outside the statutorily protected areas. More recently, the National Trust extended its land-holding by acquiring the Lifeboat Road and Ravenmeols dunes in 2017. Voluntary conservation bodies also made significant contributions, the RSPB creating Marshside Nature Reserve, while the Lancashire Wildlife Trust established reserves at Seaforth and Freshfield Dune Heath.

Protecting sites and setting up nature reserves is only part of the conservation story. Although sand-dunes and saltmarshes are amongst the most natural of our wildlife habitats, the Sefton Coast has been so modified by human activities that natural processes cannot be wholly relied upon. Therefore active management is needed to provide the full range of habitats and species. In the case of the sand-dunes, there are many threats to this diversity, arguably the most important being the overgrowth of vegetation and the associated development of scrub in

Club-house, Royal Birkdale Golf Course

Old sand quarry, Ravenmeols dunes

the last seventy years or so. As I have shown much of our rich dune flora depends on open patches (disturbed ground) to seed into, while relatively few plants can compete with dense scrub or even tall grassy swards. Analysis of aerial photos shows that, since 1945, the Sefton dunes have lost over 80% of their bare sand while scrub and young woodland-cover have increased more than six-fold. This has greatly reduced the rate of formation of new dune-slacks, many of which were created by wind-erosion of bare sand. There are many reasons for these changes which have affected coastal dunes throughout Britain and Europe and even on other continents. In Sefton, they include natural aging of vegetation over time, abandoning livestock grazing, planting of invasive non-native shrubs and trees, dune stabilisation works and the aerial deposition of nitrogen from industrial, domestic and agricultural sources. Nitrogen acts as a ferti-liser encouraging the growth of coarse grasses and scrub. Climate change may also be playing a role; longer growing seasons mean more vegetation, while wetter winters and prolonged spring droughts may have impacts yet to be determined. The demise of Rabbits, due to disease, has been especially problematic. As well as maintaining short vegetation, their burrowing in the fixed dunes brings calcium-rich soil to the surface, thereby increasing floral diversity. Some have argued that we should allow 'nature' to take its course but, if the dunes are left unmanaged, they will soon be covered in scrub and woodland, resulting in the likely extinction of a specialised, diverse and irreplaceable flora that the nation has decided should be conserved.

Although conifer plantations cover only about 12% of the system, they have a disproportionately large impact on duneland ecology. The trees shade out most of the specialist dune flora, seed into open dune habitats and increase shelter thereby encouraging the growth of scrub. They also intercept rainfall and soak up more ground-water than grassland, leading to a lowering of the water-table in their vicinity.

A related problem is the way that marine erosion along a 5 km length of Formby Point is pushing back the fore-dunes against the frontal woodlands. In the 1970s, this 'coastal squeeze' resulted in 'Gypsy Wood' at Freshfield falling into the sea. A similar fate is currently affecting another conifer compartment on Formby Golf Course. Sea-level rise (about 3 mm per annum and increasing), caused by climate change, may exacerbate coastal erosion. Meanwhile, the continuity of frontal dunes along this stretch of coast is being lost, adversely affecting its wildlife, while the trees interfere with the natural roll-back of the frontal dunes.

Cabin Hill NNR frontal dunes – no bare sand

Young secondary woodland of Grey Poplar with bramble on Birkdale sand-dunes

Gypsy Wood falling onto the beach at Freshfield in 1977 due to coastal erosion

Our saltmarshes have been less affected by human pressures, though some areas have been modified by livestock grazing which tends to reduce floral variety. However, the Ribble Estuary is silting up, so new ungrazed saltmarsh is rapidly forming between Marshside and Southport. This supports plants that would be eliminated by grazing, including the sea lavenders described earlier.

From 1890 to the 1970s, saltmarshes on the south side of the Ribble Estuary were gradually embanked and converted into farmland. Plans in 1978 to reclaim even more land, including Crossens Marsh, were resisted by conservationists, resulting in the establishment of the Ribble Estuary NNR the following year. With later additions, the reserve now covers over 5200 ha, though only about 9% lies in Sefton. The inner parts of the saltmarsh are managed by summer cattle grazing to maintain swards suitable for wintering waterbirds. As well as conserving internationally important wildlife habitat, this reserve has an enormous capacity to store carbon in its waterlogged soils. Reclaimed grazing marsh behind the Marine Drive at Marshside was taken over by the RSPB in the early 1990s, its management producing seasonally flooded pastureland with a rich variety of wildflowers, including marsh-orchids.

Crossens Marsh, Ribble Estuary National Nature Reserve

Active management of sand-dune habitats and species for nature conservation began in Ainsdale NNR during the 1960s. Since then, many different techniques have been employed to maintain suitable conditions for the specialised dune flora, including scrub control, grazing, mowing and turf stripping

Scrub control

Although scrub is a natural feature of sand-dune vegetation, there is no doubt that it has become greatly over-represented in recent decades, partly because of the decline of Rabbits, which once kept it under control. The introduced and invasive Sea Buckthorn is a major problem, its dense thickets impeding public access, eliminating most other plants and enriching the soil with nitrogen, making conditions less suitable for typical dune flora. Although it usually grows in dry soils, it will also invade the edges of wet-slacks where many of our choicest flowers are to be found. The key to controlling this shrub it to attack it early while the bushes are still young. The wood is iron-hard and stems more than about ten years old are difficult for volunteers to tackle with hand-tools. Also, the longer it is left, the more the soil is altered and the less likely it is that the dune plantlife will quickly recover after scrub removal. Cut stumps often re-grow, sometimes even after treatment with an approved herbicide. It is therefore essential to persist with annual lopping. Experience with volunteer groups is that cutting (in autumn and winter) for five or six successive years largely eliminates Sea Buckthorn from slacks, though it is more resilient in drier places. Since 2010, several floristically rich slacks and ridges in the southern Birkdale frontal dunes have been progressively cleared by volunteer 'buckthorn bashers'. Similarly, the younger sections of Birkdale Green Beach were kept completely free of Sea Buckthorn by volunteers hand-pulling hundreds of seedlings each year. Ideally, of course, the larger bushes should be pulled out by the roots, reducing the likelihood of regrowth. This requires heavy

'Buckthorn Bashers' in the Birkdale frontal dunes

Uprooting scrub in an Ainsdale LNR slack

machinery, as used by Sefton Council in 2021 at Ainsdale LNR to clear slacks that had been invaded by Sea Buckthorn and birch.

Older slacks are sometimes invaded by Grey Willow. Thus, a 1 ha slack in Cabin Hill NNR that had become dominated by 4 m-tall willows was cleared in 2005 by Natural England. Counts of annual rings showed that the trees had an average age of only 24 years. Over the next two years the slack was colonised by 139 higher plants, 11 being regionally or nationally notable and 28 new reserve records. Purple

Loosestrife put on a particularly good show. One of the rarer colonists was Blunt-flowered Rush, for which this slack is now one of the best sites on the coast.

As described earlier, the introduced Japanese Rose is another problem plant that has spread rapidly on dunes near the sea since the 1970s. A control programme began in 2016, with the aim of clearing all the bushes at Cabin Hill NNR and Altcar Training Camp. By 2021, Cabin Hill had been completed and great progress had been made in removing and burying dozens of large bushes along the Altcar frontage.

Japanese Rose control at Altcar Training Camp dunes

Purple Loosestrife proliferating in a Cabin Hill slack after removal of Grey Willow

Livestock grazing

Traditional livestock grazing was re-introduced to Ainsdale NNR in 1990, being extended since to several other dunelands, mainly during the winter season. Various 'rare-breeds' have been used, especially hardy Herdwick sheep from Cumbria. A small herd of Shetland cattle was introduced in 2008/09, while Belted Galloways, Shorthorns and Redpoll cattle have also contributed to the grazing regimes.

The aim of grazing is to control invasive scrub and open up rank grassland swards, creating a mosaic of low vegetation and small patches of bare sand. This has proved most successful on Ainsdale NNR's 'Dune Restoration Area' where trees and scrub were removed in the 1990s. Here, a combination of winter sheep grazing with year-round Rabbit activity created a wonderfully rich fixed-dune and slack vegetation. One of the plants that benefitted

was the Field Gentian. As described earlier, this species increased dramatically, research by Patricia Lockwood and me suggesting that the interaction between Rabbit and sheep grazing is crucial. Rabbits keep the sward low, while sheep prevent the build-up of leaf litter and browse the competitive Creeping Willow. Both grazers disturb the ground surface so that gentian seedlings can become established.

The distribution of Rabbits on the Sefton dunes is now patchy, large areas having few if any Rabbits. The resulting growth of coarse grassland prevents their return, as these creatures avoid coarser swards once established. It is hoped that conservation grazing by livestock can help to create the short vegetation needed for Rabbits to re-colonise.

Herdwick sheep grazing at Cabin Hill NNR

Grazing by cattle has proved invaluable on Ainsdale LNR, opening up coarse vegetation on the fixed-dunes to the benefit of low-growing flowers like Heath Dog-violet and many spring annuals. However, the cattle tended to avoid the wet slacks which were increasingly invaded by scrub. In 2021 the local authority began the daunting task of removing this, using heavy machinery to uproot the bushes and then bury them. creating valuable areas of bare sand for annuals and other low-growing plants.

Belted Galloway cattle on fixed-dunes at Ainsdale LNR

Ainsdale NNR dune restoration area

Mowing

In some senses, mowing replicates the action of grazing animals; it lowers vegetation height, giving opportunities for small, less-competitive species and may encourage the return of Rabbits. However, it can only be used where topography allows and needs to take place after the target species have finished flowering and set seed. Mowing damp dune grassland after mid-July at Altcar Training Camp resulted in a spectacular increase in Green-winged and other orchids. Cut material ('arisings') should ideally be collected and removed to maintain low soil fertility. Another example of the benefits of mowing can be seen on coastal roadside verges, some of which are extremely rich in small sand-dune plants, especially annuals such as the rare Clustered Clover.

Mowing grassland at Altcar Training Camp

Members of Liverpool Botanical Society study a mowed roadside verge at Hightown

Turf-stripping

Turf-stripping involves scraping off vegetation and top-soil down to the underlying sand. It has been much used in slacks to create shallow scrapes for Natterjack Toad breeding. This has the added benefit of producing new young habitat for pioneer slack plants. These are often scarce because most of the naturally-formed slacks are many decades old, the pioneers having been replaced by taller-growing plants. Characteristic of young scrapes are Small-fruited Yellow-sedge, Seaside Centaury, Brookweed, Bog Pimpernel and Knotted Pearlwort. As scrapes get a little older, they support marsh-orchids, Grass-of-Parnassus and Variegated Horsetail, while the deeper ones provide opportunities for Lesser Water-plantain and Tubular Water-dropwort.

Another habitat for which turf-stripping has proved beneficial is dune heath. In 2009, Lancashire Wildlife Trust removed several areas of dense Gorse in its Freshfield reserve, taking the opportunity to scrape off the nitrogen-enriched topsoil. An open, Rabbit-grazed heathland community developed; this was so successful that similar work was organised on the heath in 2016 and 2020/21.

Following ambitious projects in the Netherlands and Denmark, there is now increasing interest in using heavy machinery to re-mobilise and rejuvenate parts of overgrown coastal dunes in Britain. Increased dynamism can then produce blow-outs with new secondary dune-slacks similar to the Devil's Hole at Ravenmeols but on a smaller scale. At the time of writing (2021), the national Dynamic Dunescapes project proposes limited re-mobilisation on Ainsdale NNR, together with coastwide control of the invasive Japanese Rose.

Young Heather at Freshfield Dune Heath on an area that was turf-stripped eight years previously

Translocations and re-introductions

As a last resort, it may be necessary to take drastic action to conserve a threatened plant by moving it to a new location, taking it into cultivation for a while, or even re-introducing a species that has become extinct. This assumes a good knowledge of the plant's requirements and the presence of suitable, well-managed habitat. I have already described how the Isle of Man Cabbage was moved in 1992 from its last known site at Blundellsands just before it was destroyed by development. This resulted in two large thriving colonies in duneland at Hall Road and Crosby Coastal Park. Similarly, in 1977, I translocated rooted material of the very rare Baltic Rush × Soft Rush hybrid from the upper shore at Hightown, where it was about to be washed away, to a newly-dug scrape at Altcar Training Camp. It still survives at Altcar. The Sharp Club-rush was also saved from extinction by being cultivated at the University of Liverpool. After the colony disappeared from the Ainsdale NNR, Liverpool material was re-introduced in 1990 to dune-scrapes at Birkdale LNR. It has since prospered, spreading to new sites up to 150m away.

About 75 plants have become extinct along the Sefton Coast, many of them lost a century or more ago, before nature conservation and habitat management were thought of. Perhaps some of these could be helped to return if areas of suitable habitat can be found. Joshua Styles set up the *North West Rare Plant Initiative* in 2017 with the aim of re-introducing species where appropriate. By 2020, extinct Sefton Coast plants benefitting from the scheme included Heath Cudweed, Small Cudweed and Sheep's-bit.

Joshua Styles and Patricia Lockwood reintroducing Heath Cudweed to Birkdale Cemetery in 2019

MONITORING

It's obvious that if you don't know what you've got, you can't conserve it. Therefore monitoring the status of our wildflowers is crucial to their effective conservation. The simplest approach is to record the date, location (grid reference) and recorder's name for all significant species, sending that information, preferably in a spreadsheet, to the South Lancashire vice-county recorder, also copied to the regional recording centre (in this case Merseyside BioBank). Importantly, this is something that competent volunteers can do. More ambitious projects measure population sizes of a species at intervals, say, every five or ten years, to determine both current numbers and whether they are increasing or decreasing. Examples of this approach on the Sefton Coast include long-term studies of Baltic Rush, Common Wintergreen, Early Sand-grass, Flat-sedge and Sharp Club-rush. Also valuable are one-off surveys of particular species or habitats providing a baseline for future studies. The results of over 30 species surveys are summarised in this book.

Populations are assessed either by counting individuals or measuring the areas covered by the plant and recording the types of vegetation and soil in which it grows. In a few cases it has been possible to recruit and train teams of volunteers to carry out these studies; examples include Dune and Green-flowered Helleborine in 2008/09 and the Grass-of-Parnassus survey of 2013. Detailed habitat surveys mapped plant communities on the entire dune system in 1988/89 and 2003/04. My long-term studies have looked at changes in the plantlife of slacks in the Birkdale frontal dunes between 1983 and 2003, on Birkdale Green Beach since 1986 and at the Devil's Hole from 2004. Student projects can be a way of collecting valuable information, though the quality of the results may be variable. Most important of all is to make sure that the results of surveys are provided to land-owners and managers, copied to Merseyside BioBank and, where possible, published in an appropriate magazine or scientific journal.

Mike Wilcox and Jesse Tregale record a hybrid centaury at Cabin Hill

The author surveying Small-fruited Yellow-sedge at Altcar in 2016 (F.T. Davenport)

FURTHER READING

The Sefton Coast and its flora feature in a great number of books, articles and scientific papers, far more than I can list here. I have tried to provide the interested reader with a selection of accessible references, including historical works and articles used in the text. Most of these can be sourced online or in libraries. There are several illustrated guides to the identification of British wildflowers. Most are excellent, so I have not expressed a particular preference.

Atkinson, D. & Houston, J. (eds.) 1993. *The sand dunes of the Sefton Coast.* National Museums & Galleries on Merseyside.

Dempsey, J. 2016. *Sandscape: the cultural and natural heritage of the Sefton Coast.* Sefton Coast Landscape Partnership

Edmondson, S.E. 1997. *Key to plants common on sand dunes.* Aidgap guide, Field Studies Council, Shrewsbury.

Greenwood, E.F. (ed.) 1999. *Ecology and landscape development: A natural history of the Mersey basin.* Liverpool University Press/National Museums & Galleries on Merseyside.

Houston, J.A., Edmondson, S.E. & Rooney, P.J. (eds.) 2001. *Coastal dune management: shared experience of European conservation practice.* Liverpool University Press, Liverpool.

McNicholl, E.D. (ed.) 1883. *Handbook for Southport.* 3rd edition. Robert Johnson, Southport.

Michell, P.E. & Smith, P.H. 2012. Distribution, ecology and conservation of Epipactis dunensis in the sand-dunes of the Sefton Coast, Merseyside. *BSBI News* 120: 6-16.

Packham, J.R. & Willis, A.J. 1997. *Ecology of dunes, salt marsh and shingle.* Chapman & Hall, London.

Ranwell, D.S. 1972. *Ecology of salt marshes and sand dunes.* Chapman & Hall, London.

Savidge, J.P., Heywood, V.H. & Gordon, V. (eds.) 1963. *Travis's flora of South Lancashire.* Liverpool Botanical Society.

Sefton Coast Landscape Partnership (undated). *Sefton's wild flowers. A guide to 30 of the coast-line's special plants.*

Smith, P.H. 2000. Classic wildlife sites: The Sefton Coast sand-dunes, Merseyside. *British Wildlife* 12: 28-36.

Smith, P.H. 2007. The Birkdale Green Beach – a sand-dune biodiversity hotspot. *British Wildlife* 19: 11-16.

Smith, P.H. 2008. Increase in Dune Wormwood (Artemisia campestris ssp. maritima) at Crosby sand-dunes, Merseyside. *BSBI News* 107: 28-29.

Smith, P.H. 2008. *Corynephorus canescens* (L.) P. Beauv. on the Sefton Coast, Merseyside. *Watsonia* 27: 149-157.

Smith, P.H. 2008. Population explosion of *Hypochaeris glabra* L. on the Sefton Coast, Merseyside in 2007. *Watsonia* 27: 159-166.

Smith, P.H. 2009. The *Sands of time revisited: An introduction to the sand dunes of the Sefton Coast.* Amberley Publishing, Stroud.

Smith, P.H. 2010. Tubular Water-dropwort on the Sefton Coast sand-dunes, Merseyside. *BSB. News* 113: 13-17.

Smith, P.H. 2010. Changing status of *Eleocharis uniglumis* on the Sefton Coast, Merseyside (v.c.59) *BSBI News* 115: 18-24.

Smith, P.H. 2012. Reserve focus: Cabin Hill NNR, Merseyside. *British Wildlife* 23: 343-347.

Smith, P.H. 2013. Changing status and ecology of *Blysmus rufus* (Saltmarsh Flat-sedge) in South Lancashire (v.c.59). *BSBI News* 123: 55-63.

Smith, P.H. 2014. *Juncus subnodulosus* (Blunt-flowered Rush) in the Sefton Coast sand-dunes Merseyside (v.c.59, South Lancashire). *BSBI News* 125: 12-17.

Smith, P.H. 2015. Revisiting Schoenoplectus pungens (Sharp Club-rush). *BSBI News* 128: 21-24.

Smith, P.H. 2017. The natural history of a sand-dune blowout. *British Wildlife* 28: 329-334.

Smith, P.H. 2017. Occurrence and ecology of Carex oederi (Small-fruited Yellow-sedge) on the Sefton Coast, Merseyside (v.c.59, South Lancashire). *BSBI News* 135: 22-28.

Smith, P.H. 2019. Changing status of *Blysmus compressus* (Flat-sedge) in the Sefton Coast sand-dunes, north Merseyside, UK. *British & Irish Botany* 1 (2): 70-90.

Smith, P.H. 2020. Increasing status of non-native vascular plants in the Sefton Coast sand-dune system, north Merseyside, UK. *British & Irish Botany* 2: 102-126.

Smith, P.H. & Cross, S. 2016. Effect of mowing regime on abundance of green-winged orchic *Anacamptis morio* on coastal grassland in Merseyside, England. *Conservation Evidence* 13: 79-81.

Smith, P.H. & Deed, B. 2014. A volunteer survey of *Parnassia palustris* (Grass-of-Parnassus) on the Sefton Coast, Merseyside, v.c.59. *BSBI News* 127: 5-18.

Smith, P.H. & Deed, B. 2019. Japanese Rose (*Rosa rugosa*): its invasion and colonisation of the Sefton Coast, north Merseyside, UK. *British & Irish Botany* 1: 185-201.

Smith, P.H., Highfield, C.M. & Lockwood, P.A. 2011. Changing status of *Mibora minima* on the Sefton Coast, Merseyside (v.c.59). *BSBI News* 118: 28-33

Smith, P.H. & Kimpton, A. 2008. Effects of grey willow (*Salix cinerea*) removal on the floral diversity of a wet dune-slack at Cabin Hill National Nature Reserve on the Sefton Coast, Merseyside England. *Conservation Evidence* 5: 6-11.

Smith, P.H. & Lockwood, P.A. 2010. Monitoring Sea Bindweed (*Calystegia soldanella*) on the Sefton Coast, Merseyside in 2010. *BSBI News* 115: 25-29.

Smith, P.H. & Lockwood, P.A. 2011. Grazing is the key to the conservation of *Gentianella campestris* (L.) Börner (Gentianaceae): evidence from the north Merseyside sand-dunes. *New Journal o. Botany* 1: 127-136.

Smith, P.H. & Lockwood, P.A. 2012. Investigations into a previously unknown population of Black Poplar (*Populus nigra* ssp. *betulifolia*) at Formby Point, Merseyside. *BSBI News* 121: 23-34.

Smith, P.H. & Lockwood, P.A. 2012. Lesser Water-plantain in the Sefton Coast sand-dunes. *BSB News* 120: 31-36.

Smith, P.H. & Lockwood, P.A. 2014. *Trifolium glomeratum* (Clustered Clover) in north-west England *BSBI News* 124: 35-36.

Smith, P.H. & Lockwood, P.A. 2016. Status of Juncus balticus (Baltic Rush) and its hybrids in England. *BSBI News* 131: 8-16.

Smith, P.H. & Lockwood, P.A. 2016. Changing status of *Coincya monensis* ssp. *monensis* (Isle of Man Cabbage) on the Sefton Coast (v.c.59, South Lancashire). *BSBI News* 133: 18-24.

Smith, P.H. & Lockwood, P.A. 2017. Exceptional population of *Teesdalia nudicaulis* in v.c.59. *BSBI News* 136: 17-19.

Smith, P.H. & Lockwood, P.A. 2018. Changing status of *Pyrola minor* (Common Wintergreen) on the Sefton Coast, Merseyside (v.c.59). *BSBI News* 138: 31-36.

Smith, P.H. & Wilcox, M.P. 2016. Willows (*Salix*) on the Sefton Coast, north Merseyside (v.c.59, South Lancashire). *BSBI News* 132: 14-18.

Stace, C.A. 2019. *New flora of the British Isles fourth edition*. C & M Floristics, Suffolk.

Styles, J., Smith, P.H., Lockwood, P.A. & Hunt, N. 2019. Changing status of *Scleranthus annuus* (Annual Knawel) on the Sefton Coast, north Merseyside. *BSBI News* 142: 22-26.

Whittle, P. 1831. *Marina; or a historical and descriptive account of Southport, Lytham and Blackpool, situate on the western coast of Lancashire*. P. & H. Whittle, Preston.

Worsley, A.T., Lymbery, G., Holden, V.J.C. & Newton, M. (eds.) 2010. *Sefton's dynamic coast*. Sefton Technical Services Department, Southport.

Heath Dog-violet (*Viola canina*), a Red-listed plant frequent on the Sefton dunes

Appendix 1. Scientific names of plants referred to in the text

* = non-native or introduced native.
Nomenclature follows C.A. Stace's *New Flora of the British Isles fourth edition* (2019).
Note: small-case letters are used for species groups (e.g. bluebell, evening-primrose)

Vernacular name	Scientific name	Page number
Adder's-tongue	*Ophioglossum vulgatum*	78, 84
Alder	*Alnus glutinosa*	14, 15, 39, 40, 74
Annual Knawel	*Scleranthus annuus*	37
Atlantic Scurvy-grass	*Cochlearia atlantica*	10
Autumn Gentian	*Gentianella amarella*	70
Babington's Orache	*Atriplex glabriuscula*	18
Balm-of-Gilead*	*Populus ×jackii*	40, 55
Baltic Rush	*Juncus balticus*	2, 62, 65, 66, 73, 74, 78, 80, 85, 99, 100
Baltic Rush × Hard Rush	*Juncus ×lancastriensis*	62, 80
Baltic Rush × Soft Rush	*Juncus ×obotritorum*	85, 99
Beaked Hawk's-beard*	*Crepis vesicaria*	21
Bee Orchid	*Ophrys apifera*	26, 27, 78, 80, 84
Bird's-foot	*Ornithopus perpusillus*	24, 25, 38, 44, 45, 82
Biting Stonecrop	*Sedum acre*	16, 17, 85
Black Bog-rush	*Schoenus nigricans*	54
Black Poplar*	*Populus nigra* subsp. *betulifolia*	40, 41
Blue Fleabane	*Erigeron acris*	24
bluebell	*Hyacinthoides*	61
Blunt-flowered Rush	*Juncus subnodulosus*	46, 78, 95
Bog Pimpernel	*Lysimachia tenella*	51, 52, 98
Bogbean	*Menyanthes trifoliata*	78, 79, 80
Bohemian Knotweed*	*Reynoutria ×bohemica*	56
Broad-leaved Everlasting-pea*	*Lathyrus latifolius*	56, 57
Brookweed	*Samolus valerandi*	15, 98
Brown Sedge	*Carex disticha*	74, 78, 80
Bugloss	*Lycopsis arvensis*	27, 28, 85
Bulrush	*Typha latifolia*	14
Burnet Rose	*Rosa spinosissima*	26, 85
Buttonweed*	*Cotula coronopifolia*	12
Carline Thistle	*Carlina vulgaris*	24
Cat's-ear	*Hypochaeris radicata*	21, 33, 44
Changing Forget-me-not	*Myosotis discolor*	81
Clustered Clover	*Trifolium glomeratum*	38, 98
Common Bent	*Agrostis capillaris*	44
Common Bird's-foot-trefoil	*Lotus corniculatus*	24, 25, 38
Common Centaury	*Centaurium erythraea*	24, 63
Common Cord-grass	*Spartina anglica*	10
Common Couch	*Elymus junceiformis*	12

Vernacular name	Scientific name	Page number
Common Glasswort	*Salicornia europaea*	10
Common Meadow-rue	*Thalictrum flavum*	12, 85
Common Nettle	*Urtica dioica*	61
Common Polypody	*Polypodium vulgare*	28
Common Ragwort	*Jacobaea vulgaris*	21
Common Reed	*Phragmites australis*	12, 14, 66
Common Restharrow	*Ononis repens*	21, 24
Common Saltmarsh-grass	*Puccinellia maritima*	10, 12, 14
Common Sea-lavender	*Limonium vulgare*	10, 11, 71
Common Spike-rush	*Eleocharis palustris*	87
Common Spotted × Early Marsh-orchid	*Dactylorhiza ×kernerorum*	63
Common Spotted × Southern Marsh-orchid	*Dactylorhiza ×grandis*	63
Common Spotted-orchid	*Dactylorhiza fuchsii*	63
Common Stork's-bill	*Erodium cicutarium*	28
Common Twayblade	*Neottia ovata*	84
Common Wintergreen	*Pyrola minor*	42, 100
Corsican Pine*	*Pinus nigra* subsp. *laricio*	40, 55
Cowslip	*Primula veris*	35
Creeping Thistle	*Cirsium arvense*	21
Creeping Willow	*Salix repens*	47, 62, 67, 83, 96
Creeping Willow × Osier	*Salix ×friesiana*	62, 83
Creeping Willow × Osier × Grey Willow	*Salix ×angusensis*	62
Crowberry	*Empetrum nigrum*	44
Cypress Spurge*	*Euphorbia cyparissias*	61
Daffodil*	*Narcissus*	59
Dandelion	*Taraxacum*	21, 29, 33
Dewberry	*Rubus caesius*	28
Don's Willow	*Salix ×doniana*	62, 83, 85
Dove's-foot Crane's-bill	*Geranium molle*	38
Downy Birch	*Betula pubescens*	40
Downy Oat-grass	*Avenula pubescens*	33
Drooping Star-of-Bethlehem*	*Ornithogalum nutans*	59, 60
Dune Helleborine	*Epipactis dunensis*	2, 6, 42, 67, 72, 78, 84
Dune Pansy	*Viola tricolor* subsp. *curtisii*	21, 23, 80
Dune Wormwood	*Artemisia crithmifolia*	2, 4, 69, 87
Dyer's Greenweed	*Genista tinctoria*	26, 27
Eared Willow	*Salix aurita*	44
Early Crocus*	*Crocus tommasinianus*	59
Early Forget-me-not	*Myosotis ramosissima*	28, 29, 30
Early Marsh-orchid	*Dactylorhiza incarnata*	12, 35, 49, 50, 63, 76, 84
Early Sand-grass	*Mibora minima*	2, 29, 30, 68, 72, 100
English Scurvy-grass	*Cochlearia anglica*	10
Evening-primrose*	*Oenothera*	58, 87
False Oat-grass	*Arrhenatherum elatius*	33

Vernacular name	Scientific name	Page number
Spanish Bluebell*	*Hyacinthoides hispanica*	61
Spear-leaved Orache	*Atriplex prostrata*	12, 18
Spreading Meadow-grass	*Poa humilis*	21
Spring Sedge	*Carex caryophyllea*	82
Spurge-laurel*	*Daphne laureola*	84
Squill*	*Scilla*	59
Star-of-Bethlehem*	*Ornithogalum angustifolium*	59, 60
Sticky Stork's-bill	*Erodium aethiopicum*	28
Strawberry Clover	*Trifolium fragiferum*	53, 74, 75
Summer Snowflake*	*Leucojum aestivum* subsp. *pulchellum*	59
Sweet Vernal-grass	*Anthoxanthum odoratum*	28
Sycamore*	*Acer pseudoplatanus*	40
Taschereau's Orache	*Atriplex ×taschereaui*	12
Thrift	*Armeria maritima*	14
Trailing St John's-wort	*Hypericum humifusum*	44
Triplet Lily*	*Triteleia laxa*	87, 88
Tubular Water-dropwort	*Oenanthe fistulosa*	54, 76, 98
Umbellate Hawkweed	*Hieracium umbellatum*	21
Variegated Horsetail	*Equisetum variegatum*	53, 76, 78, 98
Viper's-bugloss	*Echium vulgare*	26, 85
Wavy Hair-grass	*Avenella flexuosa*	44
White Poplar*	*Populus alba*	40, 55
White Stonecrop*	*Sedum album*	56
Whorl-grass	*Catabrosa aquatica*	82
Wild Carrot	*Daucus carota*	33
Wild Celery	*Apium graveolens*	15, 74
Wild Parsnip	*Pastinaca sativa*	33
Wild Strawberry	*Fragaria vesca*	28
Wild Thyme	*Thymus polytrichus*	31
Willow-leaved Cotoneaster*	*Cotoneaster salicifolius*	60
Wood Sage	*Teucrium scorodonia*	28
Wood Small-reed	*Calamagrostis epigejos*	33, 35
Yellow Bartsia	*Parentucellia viscosa*	3, 53
Yellow Bird's-nest	*Hypopitys monotropa*	47
Yellow Glasswort	*Salicornia fragilis*	10
Yellow Horned-poppy	*Glaucium flavum*	16, 85
Yellow Iris	*Iris pseudacorus*	74, 78, 79
Yellow Oat-grass	*Trisetum flavescens*	33
Yellow-wort	*Blackstonia perfoliata*	24

Dune Fescue, Birkdale frontal dunes

Hare's-foot Clover, Hightown dunes

Knotted Clover, Ainsdale dunes

Seaside Centaury, Birkdale Green Beach
(Trevor Davenport)

Isle of Man Cabbage, Hall Road